THE STORY OF
MARGARINE

By S. F. Riepma

Public Affairs Press, Washington, D. C.

TO MARVA

Published by Public Affairs Press
419 New Jersey Ave., S.E., Washington, D.C. 20003
Copyright, 1970, by S. F. Riepma
Printed in the United States of America
Library of Congress Card No. 70-139861

Foreword

Margarine was first prepared a century ago. It was devised by a French chemist, Hippolyte Mège-Mouriéz, who had responded to an offer by Louis Napoleon III of a prize for the production of a satisfactory substitute for butter. In the new product, Mège had used margaric acid, a fatty acid component isolated in 1813 by Michael Eugène Chevreul and named because of the lustrous pearly drops that reminded him of the Greek word for pearl—margarites.

Mège recognized the need for a name for his new product and because he had used so much margaric acid, coined the word margarine. The name is, like the food itself, an invention. Because beef fat had also been used in this first successful margarine, the prefix "oleo" from the Latin *oleum* was attached. While today's modern product is still designated margarine, the older term oleo-margarine is occasionally heard, usually inappropriately.

Dr. Riepma's book—simple, clear, and direct—explores the fascinating first century of the story of margarine in a detailed, informative, and interesting manner. From its beginnings as a substitute food (though Mège never regarded it as such), margarine has emerged as a practical, nutritious food in its own right. No food has a more impressive history and few have been the subject of more legislative enactments and court decisions. A most interesting summary of this unique legal history contributes to the understanding of today's margarine.

Nutritionally, today, margarine has emerged as a key food for persons on diets designed to contain higher amounts of polyunsaturated fats. Such diets are recommended for persons with elevated levels of blood cholesterol and who are considered an increased risk for cardiovascular diseases. In addition to this special property of providing generous quantities of polyunsaturates, margarines provide calories and fat soluble vitamin A, the latter because it is added to all margarines. Many types of margarines are available in the market today and the consumer may choose which one more suitably fits his special needs and taste.

The discussion in this book of the ingredients used in margarine manufacture and the nutritional contributions will be valuable reading for the nutritionist and physician.

The increased use of margarine today can be accounted for, in part, by repeal of restrictive trade regulations and taxes, favorable pricing, and general recommendation by the medical profession. The student of marketing will be interested in the sections in this book which discuss the manufacture and distribution of this product of which 10.8 lbs. per person was produced in the United States in 1969.

Consciously or unconsciously, the consumer judges a margarine by its "flavor, spreadability, and its melting and proper release of flavor on hot or cold foods—as a spread, seasoning or shortening. It should resist spattering, have even color, and the right degree of saltiness. It must be able to stay fresh at home under normal refrigeration temperatures for a reasonable time. It shouldn't melt or change flavor too quickly when exposed." These are the credentials that each manufacturer must meet. Add to these consumer demands the necessary testing, selection of formulas, federal standards, federal and state laws and cost structures; all are a necessary part of the story of margarine.

Dr. Riepma has provided a real service by assembling and telling this story in a manner that is accurate and readily understandable.

FREDRICK J. STARE, M.D.
Professor of Nutrition
Chairman, Department of Nutrition
Harvard School of Public Health
Boston, Massachusetts

Preface

As president of the National Association of Margarine Manufacturers, I have received many inquiries about margarine—its origin, history, manufacture, consumption, and related laws. In these pages I have brought together the story of this popular article of food in a manner that will, I trust, be useful to consumers, home economists, physicians, and others.

To acknowledge my indebtedness to everyone who has been helpful in connection with the preparation of this book is not possible. However, I wish to thank especially, for their encouragement and assistance, the members of the National Association of Margarine Manufacturers and the members of the association's Technical Committee.

I also wish to acknowledge the assistance and insight of their specialized fields contributed by Mr. Frederick G. Berner of the Market Research Corporation of America, Inc.; Mr. A. Braakman, Unilever N.V., Rotterdam, Holland; Mr. Nelson Eddy, CPC International, Inc.; Mr. Oliver J. Fiala, Durkee-Glidden Division, SCM Corporation; Mr. Harvey James, J. H. Filbert, Inc.; Mr. Dean W. Jones, J. Walter Thompson Co.; Mr. N. T. Joyner, Votator Division of the Chemetron Corporation; Mr. Harold V. Knight, Consultant; Mr. George W. Kromer of the Agricultural Research Service of the U. S. Department of Agriculture; Mr. Richard J. Leighton; Mr. Richard Meyer, U. S. Food and Drug Administration; Mrs. Evelyn Norris of the Agricultural Research Service of the U. S. Department of Agriculture; Dr. E. E. Rice, Swift & Co.; Mr. H. Keith Ridgway and Mr. J. Bryan Stine, Kraft Foods Co., Division of Kraftco Corporation; Mr. Ashley Sellers, Sellers, Conner & Cuneo; Mr. Buford L. Thomas, B. L. Thomas Associates; Dr. J. H. van Stuijvenberg, University of Utrecht; Dr. J. Sevenster, Unilever N. V.; Mr. William M. Strickland and Mr. Walter Meyer, Proctor & Gamble Co.; and Dr. Philip L. White, Council on Foods and Nutrition of the American Medical Association.

For helpful preparation of the manuscript I thank Mrs. Patricia M. Kitchen and Miss Katie S. Lee.

Most of the editorial cartoons included in the work are reproduced from original drawings collected over the years by the National Association of Margarine Manufacturers. They offer some insight into the role public opinion has played in the history of margarine. While the humor of the artists remains, the controversy they reflected has, of course, disappeared. Wherever possible the cartoons are appropriately credited, but in some instances it has been difficult to ascertain who drew them or the names of the papers in which they appeared.

S. F. RIEPMA

Washington, D. C.

Contents

Introduction

This is the story of margarine, one of our most familiar foods.

Its consumption has in recent years increased to such an extent that margarine is now the leading table spread. The American people are using more than twice as much of it as they are of butter, and this new food pattern is not likely to change. The once neglected city cousin of the spread family is now the mainstay. Its name is a familiar household word.

Whole new generations have been brought up almost entirely on the "vegetable spread." Newspapers and broadcasters told the country about the product when Congress and many state legislatures at length debated its merits and its right to be free of legal restraints. Now millions regard it as an everyday food of highest quality. Scientists and nutritionists, and often the family doctor, recommend its use in general and in specific diets.

American farmers, whose opposition fanned decades of legislative drives against the product, now recognize margarine as a significant outlet for major edible oils and fats. Food manufacturers, observing the product's success in the stores, are busy seeking new products that will follow its example by utilizing lower-cost ingredients and compete with established foods.

So it isn't surprising that most consumers already have considerable first-hand knowledge of margarine. It has acquired a new status in the public mind.

These are the more important things about margarine that have become familiar to tens of millions of America's housewives:

• It's a spread prepared to be like butter in appearance and taste and function, but, unlike butter, it is made from vegetable or other oils.

• Its most familiar packaging is in four quarters wrapped in a one-pound carton. Softer-textured margarine is sometimes packaged in small "tubs." Margarine is also wrapped in half- or full-pound rectangular prints or cylinders.

• The product name—most often "margarine" but sometimes "oleomargarine"—is always on the accompanying label which also specifies each of the ingredients included.

• Margarine's price is always less than butter's, although different margarines have different prices.

A hundred years ago, margarine was brought into existence for reasons this book will explore. Then, as now, butter supplies were inadequate to meet the requirements of growing populations. Butter had become too expensive for most people.

So margarine was devised. It is the only popular staple food to have come into existence in this direct, practical way.

First it appeared in a crude form thought up by a French chemist—Hippolyte Mège-Mouriéz. He responded promptly to an offer by Louis Napoleon III of a prize for the production of a satisfactory butter substitute. That was a long century ago. Soon the new product began to be sold in Western Europe and in the United States where it became known as "oleomargarine."

For many years it was fated to live an uncertain life despite its obvious advantages. Even as late as the middle of the present century stringent laws and blatant propaganda were mounted against the low-cost substitute. Not until 1950 did the anti-oleomargarine laws begin to crumble.

Throughout most of its history in the United States, oleomargarine was looked upon as the "poor man's butter," not considered to be as good as good dairy butter. There was some snobbery in the comparison, for the "oleo" of the Gilded Age was a frank substitute in the way it was sold and regarded. Americans accustomed to lavish natural resources did not value substitution the way our consumer economy does today. Even oleomargarine's lower price caused it to seem, by the values of yesterday, somehow inferior. Though grandmother might have had it in the kitchen, she probably wouldn't have placed it on her table except in shortage periods, like World War I.

But granddaughter does have margarine on the table today. Her ideas about margarine as a food with real credentials are

A cartoon in Beach's Magazine, March 1912

sharply changed from the old pattern. It's different—as is her way of life. Three-fourths of the table spread offered in the stores she patronizes is margarine.

Improved manufacturing technology, an expanding public demand for table spread, and the lifting of legal limitations to its sale have contributed to margarine's development in product and mass sales comparing favorably with the excellent but rather staid and unchanging characteristics of butter. At the same time margarine has preserved and in some ways improved the traditional attributes of its dairy prototype—spreadability, flavor, and nutrition.

Margarine's differences from traditional butter spread are reflected in new types. Actually there are various *margarines* with distinct differences. Imagination and science have been applied. The newer margarines look like, taste like, and are used like butter—but they do some other things, too.

Thus margarine is no longer a simple substitute for butter, unless one thinks of it that way because it does the same job for less money. Nor is its evolution completed. There will continue to be new margarines as manufacturers compete for consumer favor.

Some people, of course, like butter. Some like margarine. Both are excellent foods, uniquely competitive. Together they offer a choice that is distinctly to the consumer's advantage.

Perhaps because of its increasing popularity, consumers are asking for more information about this spread. The aim of this book is to relate the important facts of the whole margarine story—and also to correct some outworn misconceptions that still linger.

The chapters that follow are arranged according to the main subjects: the ingredients, manufacture, distribution, and nutritional values. In addition there are provided brief summaries of margarine law and history.

Initially a definition is in order. This food has changed so much that even its once popular name, "oleomargarine," has given way to "margarine."

Definitions of Margarine

Dictionary definitions of margarine are not as helpful as they should be. Some are out of date. Some are too abbreviated. One typical short definition says it is "a blend of various fats and other ingredients used as a substitute for butter." Margarine is not quite that simple nor is it an unqualified substitute.

One of the more up-to-date dictionaries gives a good working definition: "A butterlike product made of refined vegetable oils, sometimes blended with animal fats, and emulsified, usually with milk." [1] A completely adequate definition, however, should take the following into account:

Margarine is a flavored food that is 80 per cent fat, made by blending selected oils and fats with other ingredients, and usually fortified with vitamin A, to provide a spread and cooking fat that serves the purpose of butter but is different in composition and certain characteristics.

The definitions of margarine in science and law are also important.

Food technologists and chemists view it as "a solid emulsion of a fatty phase, consisting of a mixture of vegetable and animal fats and oils, and an aqueous phase, either specially prepared skim milk or water or a mixture of these and various ingredients." [2]

Very significant have been and still are the definitions of margarine established in federal and state laws, old and new. Their original intent was often punitive. To restrain the sale of the unwanted "butter substitute," lawmakers after about 1876 identified margarine (or oleomargarine, the then common name) as anything that resembled butter but was not butter. Such statutory definitions often consist of lists of ingredients (some no longer used), and they incorporate product names that now seem antique: "artificial butter," and so on.

The most important legal definition is in the federal Margarine Act of 1950. This is the law by which Congress abolished federal taxes on oleomargarine. It says that margarine (or oleomargarine) is "all substances, mixtures and compounds which

have a consistence similar to that of butter and which contain
any edible fats and oils or fats other than milk fat if made in
imitation or semblance of butter." [3]

The federal government has its official "Definition and Standard of Identity for Margarine." This can be considered a veritable declaration of independence because it established the
spread as a food in its own right, and not as an imitation or
substitute. The Standard was promulgated by the United States
Food and Drug Administration in 1941. It has been adjusted
from time to time to reflect the advent of new approved ingredients and will be more fully described later on.

As a definition it is a kind of minimum descriptive requirement
which applies to all margarines. It is not, of course, a recipe.
Margarine, it states, is "the plastic food" prepared with one or
more of a number of ingredients which are listed. An important
requirement is that margarine must be at least 80 per cent fat.[4]
There is another virtually identical Standard for animal fat margarine, promulgated and administered by the United States
Department of Agriculture.

These ways of identifying margarine restrict it to being a
spread that is four-fifths fat, made of certain ingredients, and
carefully distinguished from butter despite the close resemblance
in appearance and flavor.

The Name "Margarine"

The word "margarine" is, like the food itself, an invention.
Like most made-up words ("automobile," for instance), its roots
are in the classical languages.

The history of margarine began near the end of the Napoleonic Wars when a young French chemist, Michel Eugène
Chevreul, analyzed the fatty acids that are the building blocks
of fats. He singled out one and named it "margaric acid" because it glistened with lustrous pearly drops that reminded him
of the Greek word for pearl—*margarites* ("Margaret," inciden-
tally, has the same root).

When fellow Frenchman Mège-Mouriéz, the previously mentioned originator of margarine, completed his work, he recognized the need for some name for the new food to separate it from butter which it so closely resembled. Because his product was largely composed of Chevreul's margaric acid, he called it "margarine." Then he added the prefix "oleo," a name for beef fat (from the Latin *oleum*) because that, in a purified form, was his principal ingredient. The name "oleomargarine" became fixed in the United States until the advent of all-vegetable margarines during the 1930's. Americans learned to use the slangy abbreviation "oleo" and still frequently do, especially in rural areas.

Gradually the name "margarine", which had already achieved legal recognition in Europe, became the favored word. To purists "oleomargarine" means margarine only when it has meat fat in it. In law the two terms are regarded as synonymous.

The pronunciation of the name usually favors the soft "g"— "mar'-*j*areen." Sometimes one hears the "g" hard, as in England—"mar'-*g*ar-een."

CHARACTERISTICS AND CLASSES

Margarine is, then, a food made with scientific precision and within a legal standard. Such precision causes it to be fairly uniform and standardized in some characteristics: appearance (yellow color), general ease of spreading on bread, preponderance of sale in one-pound packages, functions, amount of calories and vitamin A, and ingredients labeling.

The main, generally shared characteristics are these:

1. It is 80 per cent fat. Most often it is made of one or more vegetable oils, but sometimes there is a mixture of vegetable and animal fat. In addition there are all animal fat margarines.

2. It is about 17 to 18½ per cent liquid, the liquid usually being pasteurized skim milk which may be cultured to create flavor. Some are made with water and some with soybean protein fluid.

3. It usually contains about 1½ to 3 per cent salt. Some are without salt.

4. It always contains a minimum of 15,000 United States Pharmacopeia units of vitamin A per pound. Some margarines also add vitamin D.

5. Other ingredients may be present in small amounts, specified by the Standards, to improve usefulness and keeping qualities. They are labeled by their specific names.

The product name is on the principal panel of the package, often on more than one panel, and the list of ingredients is close to it.

Considerable product specialization gives rise to major distinctions between the varieties of margarine. This is an outline according to major differences:

1. Differences in the type of fat that is used:
   Only vegetable oils—whether a single oil or (more often) a combination. Most margarines are in this class, or
   Only animal fats, or
   One or more vegetable oils blended with one or more animal fats.
2. Other differences in composition:
   Milk, cream, soy milk, or water, instead of skim milk.
   Higher content of polyunsaturates. Low-salt. Vegetarian (all vegetable ingredients). Kosher. Low-fat or "diet" margarine.
3. Differences in the texture or melting point or spreadability:
   Plastic or solid at room temperature—most margarines are this type.
   Soft, usually in tubs. These are newer margarines.
   Whipped, usually in sticks.
   Liquid, in a bottle-type container. There are only a few liquid margarines in current distribution.
4. Differences in the intended end use:
   Table or consumer margarine, sold at retail—the great majority of margarine is of this category.
   Industrial or commercial margarines, prepared for use by institutions, commercial bakeries, etc.
   Individual pats for restaurant serving.

5. Differences in brands and price:
House or proprietary brands, which include premium brands, the top bracket of margarines; and regular brands, comprising, generally, a middle price bracket. Store or private label brands make up a lower-price category.

Some of these categories are minor in terms of the quantity of margarines involved—for example, liquid and vegetarian margarines.

Types of Margarine

The great bulk of all margarine consumed in the United States is of these broad types:

1. *Conventional margarines* (sometimes called regular margarines but not in the price sense as that term is used elsewhere) are the most commonly sold. Their general characteristic is that they are of the familiar plastic or solid texture. Most come in one-pound (net weight) cartons, enclosing four quarter-pound sticks, each separately wrapped in foil or parchment and labeled. Some, however, are solid one-pound rectangular or half-pound, rectangular or cylindrical; these frequently are wrapped in parchment paper without an enclosing carton.

The oils and fats in these margarines have been partially hardened to cause the product to be firm and capable of being cut with a knife at room temperature—the traditional consistency of medium-hard butter—although margarines as a rule are less crumbly and more softly spread than butter. As noted in the outline of general characteristics, most conventional margarines are composed of vegetable oils only; some of only one, usually cottonseed oil, corn oil, or soybean oil. Some use combinations of vegetable oils, and some use combinations of vegetable oils and animal fats, or (in lower-priced brands) only the latter.

These margarines are sold in all the brand and price brackets. They are all-purpose, and may be used for table spread, cooking, or baking, and for seasoning or pan frying.

2. *Soft margarines* are soft in texture or consistency and therefore more spreadable and spoonable. They are nearer to the liquid state than are the conventional, plastic types. They also

contain more liquid oil which causes them to be higher in poly-unsaturates, an aspect described in Chapter V.

Their softness requires that these products be sold in dishlike tubs instead of the usual rectangular prints or quarter-pound units. Such containers usually contain one-half pound net weight although there is also a pound size. A protective sleeve-type carton is usually furnished around two half-pound tubs when the sale unit is one pound, which is usually the case.

Soft margarines are always vegetable oil products. They are all-purpose. Their formulas and their special packaging often cause them to be sold in the higher price brackets.

3. *Whipped margarines* have had their volume expanded by 50 per cent by whipping them with an inert and harmless gas. Their weight is same, pound for pound and ounce for ounce, as that of conventional soft margarines, but their volume is greater.

A given helping of whipped margarine will contain less fat and calories than the others possess. The expanded size also makes it necessary to pack whipped margarine in six sticks of one-sixth pound each in the pound carton, which is the unit of sale.

Whipped margarines also are all-purpose. They are more easily spread than regular margarines. Because their fat content, per volume measure is a third less than in conventional or soft products, the quantity used in cooking must be adjusted accordingly.

4. *Low fat margarines*—usually called diet margarines—are distinct from all other forms in two respects. The main difference is that they usually contain about half the fat of other margarines. Thus, their fat content is about 40 per cent of the total weight of the product.

Their other difference is in the name. As federal law now stands, they must be labeled "imitation margarine" although they are in no real sense imitations but are simply lower in fat. The reason for this is that they do not fit into the Standard and there is no other Standard to cover them. However, most such margarines are made according to the Standard except for the amount of fat and the name on the label.

5. Industrial margarine is prepared for commercial use, such as in bakeries or institutions. Sometimes it goes by the names "puff paste" or "baker's margarine." Such margarines are used as shortening. A slight deviation from the Standard can cause such a product to lose its legal identity as margarine and be labeled shortening or something else, even though it is "margarine" in every real respect, including appearance and taste.

The widespread use of shortenings in the United States is a big reason why margarine consumption per capita here is less than in European countries, where margarine is substantially devoted to baking use.

Industrial margarine ordinarily is conventional margarine except for its packaging, which is in bulk and does not fall into the requirements for home, kitchen or table margarines.

The five types that have been described are mutually exclusive. There are, however, certain other classifications pertaining to margarine products that are important to consumers. They cut across the classes that have been defined above, for they may embody the characteristics of conventional or soft or other forms.

1. Special margarine is a term originating with medical writers to identify margarines made with a higher than usual proportion of polyunsaturated fat (which is described in Chapter V). They may be conventional, soft, or in other forms. Nearly always they are sold in one-pound packages and are all-purpose.

The level of polyunsaturated fat in a special margarine may be as high as 30 per cent of total fat content, or higher. Special margarines usually have a ratio of polyunsaturates to saturates of 1.25 to 1. In some cases they have an even higher ratio. Such proportions are achieved by utilizing vegetable oils naturally rich in polyunsaturates, especially corn oil and safflower oil, and by emphasizing liquid or less hardened oils, which are usually higher in polyunsaturated fatty acids.

Because the oils employed may be more expensive than others, they increase the cost of special margarines. Many physicians recommend such margarines for patients confined to special diets because of heart disease or other problems.

2. *Premium margarines* provide combinations of the special
features that have been mentioned. They may be soft or whipped; low-fat; high in polyunsaturates; composed with a special
oil or by some special oils formula. As will be described further
on, the name premium margarines also has a trade meaning of
extra quality. It is also associated with higher retail prices than
other margarines.

Margarines thus possess various differences. There are no
grades (as is the case with butter for quality characteristics
solely). Margarines are differentiated in the marketplace by
brand and each brand offers—at its price—what its maker or distributor considers to be qualities consumers desire and will buy
in a product of its price range. Behind all brands of course, there
are the Standards.

3. *Other specializations.* Finally there are the margarines
that may bear one or more of all the characteristics that have
been described but are prepared to serve a special consumer
purpose: unsalted margarines; vegeterian margarines (sub-
stituting soy milk for cow's milk), and kosher margarines.

What Consumers Mostly Use

The family of margarines is a large one and may well become
larger. The special and premium types, and the soft, whipped,
and imitation types are relative newcomers whose numbers
are growing. Nevertheless, the dominant margarine remains the
conventional type, with quality and flavor markedly improved
over the oleomargarines and margarines of twenty years or more
ago.

The following sections on manufacture, distribution, and nutrition will describe the different products from those points of
approach. However, at this point it is helpful to scale the major
types as they were reported according to 1969 production,
which is practically the same as consumption.

Table margarines of all kinds accounted for more than 92 per
cent of production. The great majority, about 89 per cent, was
in the usual one-pound package form, with about 69 per cent of

the total in the usual quarter-pound prints. Of the 89 per cent, some 15 or 16 per cent was soft margarines; about 5 per cent, other consumer margarines. Industrial margarine accounted for 8 per cent.

Figures are not available that would show what and how many margarines use this or that formula or oil. The ingredients statement on the package is the consumer's best guide.

An indication of the total employment of different oils and fats in margarine adds to the picture of margarine overall. In 1969, vegetable oils of all kinds contributed about 94 per cent of the fat in all the product manufactured. (A table of all fats and oils used in margarine for various years is in the Appendix). The principal fat ingredient by far was American soybean oil. It furnished more than three-fourths (or 77 per cent) of the vegetable fat in the product.

Corn oil contributed about nine per cent, but it has been coming up fairly fast as margarines featuring it have increased. Cottonseed oil and safflower oil registered lesser shares. Peanut oil is used in some margarines. Animal fat (which tends to fluctuate in its use in margarines) accounted for less than six per cent.

Margarine and Butter Compared

"What's the difference?" always has been one of the more common questions consumers ask about margarine—meaning, of course, the differences between it and butter—other than the price.

When the vivacious wife of Wisconsin's governor in 1967 declared that she couldn't "tell the difference," she voiced an inevitable and conventional comparison. Her listeners had assembled to witness her husband sign into law that state's legalization of yellow-colored margarine.[5]

The crux of good margarine is the flavor it provides to the consumer's palate. With it, a margarine can hope to win attention and acceptance, and premium margarines can build other features on the foundation of good flavor. Probably more work has gone into finding new ways of improving margarine flavor during the past quarter century than into any other technical part of its production.

Butter flavor brought a richly satisfying taste into what would otherwise be a much less agreeable food world. It is the reason why the spread came to be valued. In America it acquired the distinction of table spread—a separate serving dish on the table. Both butter and margarine are on the table to give savor and taste to the main dish, breads, or vegetables.

Reaction to flavor is a matter of personal taste, of course. It is intangible. What is delicious or satisfying to one person may well not be for another. The familiar distinct taste associated with butter is variable. Butter flavor as presented in margarines can be made to be uniform and can be made stronger or milder. To what extent flavor is a difference between a margarine and a butter is something only the individual consumer can decide for himself.

There are, however, certain real differences between the two spreads. The main one is obvious—margarine is composed of vegetable oils and, sometimes, animal fats, singly or in combination. Butter is always milkfat, a form of animal fat. Out of this distinction arise others.

Because it is "assembled", margarine can be a softer spread, more uniform in consistency, less expensive to produce, and fortified. The fortification is with vitamin A (and, sometimes, vitamin D) to supply a fixed minimum, pound for pound. (The vitamin content of butter is variable.) Within limits, product characteristics—for example, flavor, texture, and content of polyunsaturated fatty acids—can be manipulated.

The food energy or calories in a pound of margarine, regardless of its composition, are about the same as those in a pound of butter (3,300 per pound). Practically all margarines have a higher level of polyunsaturates than butter. Vegetable oil brands are substantially higher, and certain margarines are formulated to have very high ratios of polyunsaturates to saturates.

These distinctions add up to significant differences between the two spreads despite their flavor and other basic similarities. These differences helped upgrade margarine from being a simple substitute. New margarines have brought new features to the traditional table spread.

One result is that ideas of what table spread can be and do have changed as a result of margarine's expansion in the diet.

It is a food produced under technical control so that it is capable of being designed to achieve desired product and nutritional results.

This profound advantage means that margarines can be strongly consumer oriented. Margarines as a whole depend on successful features that appeal to buyers. Dairy butter is produced in the context of a system of milk utilization that necessarily emphasizes production and government price intervention; margarine making is a means to an end. Margarine is a table spread designed to win consumer favor, to offer choices to the consumer, and to incorporate innovations of what consumers want.

The American consumer has benefited by the development of margarine. It has remained the "less expensive spread"—its average retail price in principal cities in 1969 is reported to have been only 27.8 cents a pound compared to butter's 84.6 cents, and margarine was one of the very few foods that comparably did not follow the increase in food prices in recent years.

At the same time it has produced new products and services within the table spread field.

The story of margarine is one of a food brought into being because of human need and adapted to the requirements of modern consumers. In the course of this passage margarine has acquired a new acceptance in American life.

1. *Random House Dictionary of the English Language* (New York, 1967), p. 867.

2. A. J. C. Andersen and P. N. Williams, *Margarine* (Oxford, 2d rev. ed., 1965), p. 1.

3. Public Law 459, 81st Congress, 2d Session, Chapter 61 (26 U.S.C. 2306), § 4(f) (2).

4. The federal margarine (or oleomargarine) Standards in their latest amended forms are found as follows: general, administered by the U. S. Food and Drug Administration, 21 C.F.R. § 45.1; animal fat, administered by the

Meat Inspection Service of the U. S. Department of Agriculture, 9 C.F.R. § 328.1; liquid margarine, administered by the U.S. Food and Drug Administration, 21 C.F.R. § 45.2. They are basically the same.

An international standard for anticipated inclusion in the Codex Alimentarius of the United Nations defines margarine in its current draft as "a food in the form of a plastic or fluid emulsion which usually is of the type water/oil, produced principally from edible fats and oils, which are not or are only partly derived from milk."

5. Wausau, Wisconsin, *Record-Herald,* May 24, 1967.

II

The Farm Beginning

Margarine originates "down on the farm." Its main ingredients are grown on the land. From there the margarine story proceeds to processing and then to the finished product and the dinner table. Technology serves to improve on nature.

The major component of margarine is edible oil and fat obtained from either oil-bearing plants or, to a much less extent, the edible fat of meat animals. Affer the extraction of the oils and fats, they are purified for food use by refining. They are then processed into the spread as it is found in the store. Farm and factory are the twin "production plants."

A second major ingredient in many margarines is skim or other milk. Butter-making takes milk and subtracts the skim milk; margarine-making adds skim milk to its refined oils or fats.

There is indeed a "margarine farmland," chiefly in the Midwest and South. The principal crop is the soybean plant. Grown on millions of acres in eye-pleasing rows, this short, bushy plant may be seen in ordered symmetry from tobacco Carolinas into cotton Texas, from dairy Minnesota into sugar Louisiana.

That immense food basket, the corn belt, is also a margarine belt for here the soybean shares acreage on many a farm with the tall corn. They are both cash crops, often alternated, depending on the farmer's decision as to how he can best use his acres. Corn itself is also a source of oil for margarine. Like the soybean, the corn kernel secretes an edible oil. Farming soybeans or corn is indirectly growing for margarine.

Another source of oil for margarine is the cotton fields that extend from the Southeast across the Southwest and into Southern California. Cottonseed oil, derived from the seed of the versatile cotton plant, is employed in many margarines.

In the Far West the yellow-blossomed safflower plant, thriving in arid conditions, produces from its seed an oil for certain margarines. And from the South Atlantic states comes the peanut, providing yet another oil used in some margarines as well as in many other food products.

These oilseed crops supply most of the edible vegetable oils which, particularly since World War II, have become an important source of food and nutrition. Like all food fats, vegetable oils are a concentrated form of food energy. All those named have good proportions of polyunsaturates; corn and safflower oils are especially rich in that respect.

For many years most margarine fat was derived from animal fats. Although animal fat is still used in some margarine, it has become a minor ingredient. In 1969 its use overall was less than 6 per cent of all the fats in the product. Livestock raised on farms or ranches is of course the source of this type of food fat.

The farm contribution of margarine is a substantial one. In economic terms its production makes a significant addition to the cash income farmers receive. One estimate is that the return to American agriculture from margarine in 1969 amounted to upwards of $400 million, including oils and fats as well as the skim milk that went into the product. This is subject to many variables but it appears to be a reasonable figure.

Such a sum may seem but a small part of the billions of annual farm cash income. Nevertheless the margarine contribution to agriculture is a valued one.

For one thing, oilseeds production has expanded greatly, demanding a growing market for the resultant fats and oils. Margarine production has expanded also. In addition, it has worked as a stablizing force in the sensitive fats and oils commodity markets which are prone to surpluses and thus subject to price fluctuations. By no means has the growth of oilseeds agriculture depended exclusively on margarine, but the two have, in a real sense, gone hand in hand.

Another factor is the economic relationship between the two main components of oilseeds—the fat and the protein. The latter goes chiefly into livestock and poultry feed. The prices received

"At the Mercy of the Sacred Cow"
(Fitzpatrick in the St. Louis Post-Dispatch)

by farmers for oilseeds depend on the markets for the fat and that for protein. They are therefore linked and when the fat finds a good market, as in margarine, the protein can be priced more attractively and its marketing thereby helped.

No farmer, therefore, plants and harvests and sells just for margarine. It is an indirect buyer for part of his oilseed total product. The farm market contribution of margarine is felt through the chain of oilseed processing.

It is not possible to ascertain how many farms are producing each type of oil for a given product. However, the 1964 Agriculture Census figures are of some help. They report that 559,000 farms grew soybeans for commercial sale and 324,000 grew cotton. Commercial corn growing is carried on in almost every state. Here the margarine impact is more diffuse although the margarine market has become a growing outlet for the oil by-product. The same can be said of safflower and peanuts for commercial processing. A relatively small newcomer is sunflowerseed oil.

It would seem that a least half a million farms have a reasonable stake in margarine as an outlet for their production. All participants in this type of farming derive some benefit. The soybean producer in South Dakota may not specialize as heavily in that crop as his brother farmer in Iowa, but his market is stronger just the same. The grower in Kansas may not have a drop of the oil in his corn going into margarine but he shares in the overall effect on prices.

Oilseeds agriculture has been expanding. So has margarine consumption. Demand for the oils and fats required for the vegetable spread rose by 157 per cent in the years 1941-50. The next decade the rise was 61 per cent. Between 1961 and 1969 it showed nearly 26 per cent. The soybean crop meanwhile increased from 679 to 1,117 million bushels.

The margarine-farm relationship is one of interdependence. It is highlighted by the improvement of the spread, its successful promotion, and its widening consumer acceptance. It is a good example of what economists call "agribusiness."

Growing and Extracting

The soybean plant is a plain, unadorned blue-collar crop with an ancient Asian past. But it is a powerhouse for creating fat and protein and its expansion as a crop since World War II has been phenomenal.

Through the ages man has mostly used livestock to produce needed protein and fat. The humble soybean has the ability to provide these important dietary elements more economically and easily than cattle or other animals. It grows like any grain, is harvested for the seed (which is the bean itself), and the seed yields the protein and fat.

Most soybeans are raised to be sold as a cash crop. The processed soybean products go into margarine and other foods and livestock feed. Thus the bean helps supply beef, eggs, chicken, and so on, as well as margarine. Soybean fields have spread where King Cotton or King Corn once reigned supreme. Soybean production lends itself to mechanization of agriculture; it typifies the American agricultural revolution of our time and, in a sense, so does its partner, margarine.

The farmer's end-product is a small bean containing about 18 per cent oil (or about 11 pounds to the bushel) and 32 per cent protein in the form of the meal portion—one of the most concentrated sources of protein that exists. Once harvested the beans are usually stored in country elevators where their keeping ability is good.

In processing the beans are cleaned, cracked, their hulls removed, and the meats tempered by heat. The oil may be extracted by mechanical methods, using hydraulic or screw-type presses or expellers. A more common and modern method puts the beans in a solvent fluid that efficiently separates the oil from the protein meal. The crude oil extracted is dark in color and requires refining before it can be used in margarine. Soyban oil production in 1969 reached 7.4 billion pounds, of which margarine took about a fifth.

Soybean oil is the largest American margarine ingredient both absolutely (1,334 million pounds in 1969) and relatively

(61 per cent of all the margarine produced, by weight, and 76 per cent of all the fats or oils used in the product). It is the fundamental margarine ingredient generally but it is not un-challenged. Some formulas place a high value on other oils, either as the only margarine fat ingredient or in combinations with soybean oil. One of these is corn oil.

Corn oil margarine has become increasingly popular. In 1969 the spread's use of this oil was more than 172 million pounds, making it the second largest ingredient. Corn oil, de-rived from the germ in the kernel, is a by-product of the pro-duction of starch by the wet or dry milling processes. Being so derived the amount of oil commercially available is limited. A bushel of hybrid yellow dent corn yields about two pounds of oil; approximately 466 million pounds of the oil entered the market in 1969.

To extract the oil by wet milling, the kernels are steeped and cracked, the separated germs are washed and heated, and the oil is secured by pressing or solvent extraction. The other main product is starch instead of the protein that most oil-bearing seeds yield. In dry milling, the kernels are simply ground.

Third in importance in margarine is cottonseed oil. The preeminent margarine ingredient years ago, its use has declined as a result of changes in the cost of producing cotton. Never-theless, it is still a preferred oil in many margarine formulas, usually in combination with soybean or other oils. Cottonseed oil production depends upon the market for cotton fiber. As cotton fields have migrated West, so has the production of this oil, thereby helping make California a major state for margarine manufacture.

The picked cotton goes to the gin where the small seeds are separated from the fiber. Then the seed is cleaned, dried, its fuzz removed, and it is cracked to remove the kernel from the hull. The meats in turn are cooked and pressed or treated by a special solvent process to secure the yellow oil, usually at the rate of about 300 pounds per ton of seed. In 1969 some 1,335 million pounds of this oil were produced; margarine took about 78 million.

Less important in quantitative utilization in margarine are safflower and peanut oils. Safflower oil has achieved significance in margarine because of its high content of linoleic acid, the principal polyunsaturated fatty acid. Its production, however, is limited and its cost relatively high. About 140 million pounds entered the market in 1969; 43 million pounds or nearly 31 per cent went into margarines favoring this oil.

Peanut oil possesses a mild consistency that is prized for food use. This, and the fact that only about a fourth of the peanut crop is processed for oil, makes this oil often higher in price than the others. Its production in 1969 was 170 million pounds, about 3 million going into margarines emphasizing this oil.

Coconut oil, many years ago important in margarine, is now a negligible component. The shift to domestic ingredients was completed a generation ago.

Sunflowerseed oil, sometimes called sun oil, is a new arrival as a margarine ingredient. Never present in American margarines are marine or fish oils which are not permitted by this country's margarine Standards. They are, however, common in Canadian and in European margarines.

Vegetable oils achieved their first real importance in margarine when the process was invented to harden liquid oils enough to make them solid at room temperature. Previously solid animal fats had to be used in order to give the finished product the desired plastic consistency. Animal fats continue to be employed for some lower-priced margarines. They are valued also in some commercial baking recipes. Most of the fat so employed is lard or beef stearine.

Government food distribution programs have donated animal fat margarine because of this product's low cost.

Led by the ubiquitous soybean, these are the fats and oils that belong to the margarine family of ingredients. After extraction they undergo refining and further processing. Only then are they ready for margarine making, as described in the next chapter.

An Agricultural Alliance

The shares of the different oils selected by margarine makers have been fairly stable for a number of years, highlighted by the dominance of vegetable oils generally and soybean oil in particular. Most American margarines have a certain uniformity in this respect compared with European margarines where formulas often must be more diverse in order to accommodate changing supplies of imported oils.

The importance of margarine to agriculture is on a firm basis. When shifts in preference occur among oils used in margarine, they seem likely to be gradual and to bring about a net increase of the total used. After 1957, when corn oil and then safflower oil came onstage as margarine ingredients, one result was increased total consumption. The outlook is that the gradually extending range of margarine consumption strengthens its future as a farm market.

There have been substantial shifts in the past, however, and there could be more in the future. World War I shortages of home fats brought about a great rise in favor of coconut oil. This gave way to domestic cottonseed oil in the 1930's. In the early 1950's soybean oil, aided by research that made it a more feasible oil for margarine than previously, began to be available at a lower price.

Broad reformulations of margarine fats are possible because of the relative ease with which food oils and fats may be interchanged. Soybean and cottonseed oil, a manufacturer may find, can each fit as suitably in his formulas. With due allowance for time and manufacturing practices—there are obvious brakes on too much formula changing—he will choose the one with lower price. No manufacturer can safely disregard the cost imposed by the fat, his main ingredient. Price is a very important determinant for margarines' prices to the consumer are competitive.

The bounds on choice set by the Standards do not seriously constrain selectivity—indeed were not intended to, for the Standards are not recipes. They have an economic as well as a quality purpose, to give consumers the benefit of price differences between available fats. Competition assures this will be done within the main categories of margarines. If a given oil can meet the requirements, it can find a place in margarines. Soybean oil's top place is in good part explained by its costs. In 1969, for example, its average cost (crude) was about 10.7 cents a pound, compared with cottonseed at 11.0 cents; corn, 18.7 cents; safflower 15.6 cents; and peanut, 14.3 cents.

Margarine improvement is linked to the option to select its oils and fats. New oils—such as safflower and sunflowerseed—are introduced as a feature of new products. Most edible fats are available in abundance. However, as margarine compositions change and innovate, the farmer will continue to be a beneficiary.

THE FATS-PROTEIN COMPLEX

Food fats are not produced as such. One raises soybeans, not the component oil or protein. The cotton plant is a combination of the fiber, the primary objective, and the cottonseed, which also combines oil and protein. Livestock embody a number of foods, chiefly meat and milk, which comprise combinations of fat and protein and carbohydrates.

Thus edible fat and protein, two essential elements of human food, are derived from different sources and are joined in nature.

The economist, looking at oilseed agriculture, sees it as a system to produce fat and protein. The farmer who grows soybeans is in effect growing fat for margarine and other uses as well as protein for livestock and poultry feed or even human use. The protein fed to livestock becomes in turn, meat, milk, eggs, and other forms of protein that are human food. Some name this two-goal production system the fats-protein complex.

The generalization is not perfect. Safflower seed, for instance, is raised almost entirely for the oil in the seed. Also, not all proteins are equal in precise nutritional terms. Nevertheless the fats-protein production system is very important in modern agriculture. Margarine is a working factor in it.

The margarine role in this system remains one of a supporting actor in a play. As a taker of soybean oil the vegetable spread helps pay for the beans, gives support to the price of the oil, and indirectly helps keep a farmer's cost lower for the protein fraction which has a great share of the job of feeding livestock and poultry.

Margarine has helped the farmer meet his production cost, has helped the processor achieve a desirable balance between the prices of the fat and the protein, and indirectly has aided in the production of beef, pork, veal, milk, eggs, and poultry. The better standard of eating Americans have acquired has been based largely on a protein-oriented food economy.

All this, in turn, reflects a more efficient use of land resources. Oilseeds have replaced other crops; margarine has largely replaced butter.

Butterfat (or milkfat) is a by-product of milk production. In the manufactured form of butter it is the principal competitor of margarine for the favor of consumers. An intrinsic disadvantage of butterfat is that even as a side product of milk it is expensive to produce compared to vegetable fats. Further, butter's price is sustained by government support. Dairymen have increased their efficiency of production and their sales of products utilizing the butterfat as a component of whole milk, cheese, and ice cream.[1] But the difference in cost between sesuring edible fat from soybeans and by running feed through a cow is very considerable.

World War II food requirements emphasized the economics of getting needed food energy to consumers in the less expensive form of fat from vegetable sources. One report figured that it took one "unit" of farm resources to secure 97 pounds of fat from soybeans or 36 pounds from milk.[2] Wartime shortages have departed, and malnutrition or hunger problems at home and abroad have reinforced the search for providing more and better food at less cost. Margarine—or margarine-like foods— can be one part of the solution.

Meanwhile the once important role of butter as a storageplace for excess fat from milk has lost much of its importance.

Dairy resources have been applied more to the production of milk. Butter in 1969 took less than half the proportion of the milk supply in 1969 than in 1940. Margarine and butter both look more and more like members of the same fat-protein complex.

Much of the information on margarine as a farm product is defensive with scant mention of the consumer. In reality it is not possible to be precise about what economic benefits any reasonably large class of farmers derives from one food fat product or another; generalizations and estimates must suffice. Regardless, these comparisons have limited relevance in the consumer's mind. Modern sophisticated food markets and marketing are more concerned with what the consumer will accept, not with what agriculture produces. What is helpful is to assess the worth of a product in the whole social context— its answer to real needs of consumers as consumers today live and spend; its significance as a progressive sharer of the national nutritional requirements; its capability of participating in the interdependent farm production and marketing system; its demands on government; and its links with technology.

These considerations are applicable to the margarine situation; old antagonisms in farm history are not.

Margarine today has a new agricultural base. Its value to agriculture extends into the fats-protein complex and into sharing the promise of more scientific and efficient use of the land to create nourishing food for all income groups.

---

1. National Commission on Food Marketing, *Organization and Competition in the Dairy Industry* (Washington, 1966), 5, 6, 13 *et passim*.

2. R. P. Christiansen, *Using Resources to Meet Food Needs* (Washington, 1948), 62.

III

Making Margarine

Once an enterprising home economist contrived a simple do-it-yourself kit to illustrate how margarine is made. She devised a little set containing clear vegetable oil and some flavoring and coloring, with directions for combining these ingredients wth skim milk so as to come up with a kind of home-made spread.

She thus dramatized the ingredients and assembly of margarine—the principle of bringing together prepared fats, a liquid phase (the milk), and other substances.

To be sure, she oversimplified. Real margarine calls for sophisticated formulation from a greater number of carefully selected ingredients, under very technical conditions. It is much more than a kitchen recipe.

In the manufacture of margarine three skills must be brought into play: establishing the right emulsion, developing the right "buttery" flavor, and getting the proper "melt" of the margarine in the mouth. These are essential margarine *qualities*. There are also the margarine *parts*—fat being the principle one. The art is putting everything together to assure a pleasing table spread, plus any special features desired.[1]

A margarine plant presents no stunning array of machinery. The packaging line clatters, but on the whole it is a subdued place, modest in size as food processing plants go. There is an ordered placement of tanks and vats, criss-crossing pipelines, and a flow of packaged product going into shipping boxes. The environment is one of stainless steel, tile, and the aroma of heated fats and milk.

Much of what goes on is within a closed system hidden from sight. The key word is *balance*.

The manufacturer establishes a balance of materials, flavor

and consistency in the physical form of a solid or semi-solid emulsion. Margarine is a special water-in-oil emulsion (so is butter). The emulsion is difficult to bring about because oil is being combined with liquids—skim milk or water—that normally are not compatible with it. This marriage of unseeking partners is performed by a kind of homogenizing. The particles of oil or fat become extremely small and eventually form crystal matrixes in which tiny droplets of watery liquid are entrapped.

The fat particles or droplets must be the correct microscopic size and be dispersed to form an even, firm mass that will not leak the watery liquid. The flavor-giving elements must be distributed properly throughout the whole.

The composite mixture must balance out to a finished emulsion that—in addition to other qualities—has the right melting point, is slightly moist yet not watery, and is uniform throughout large-quantity production. The end result must meet the consumer's sense of what he wants in a table spread.

The credentials of a good margarine include flavor, spreadability, and its melting and proper release of flavor on hot or cold foods—as a spread, seasoning or shortening. It should resist spattering, have even color, and the right degree of saltiness. It must be able to stay fresh at home under normal refrigeration temperatures for a reasonable time. It shouldn't melt or change flavor too quickly when exposed.

Each manufacturer has these goals and his own tested ideas as to how to make a quality product within the requirements of his formulas, federal standards, federal and state laws, and costs.

REFINING

The crude oils and fats that come to the refiner are in varying conditions of purity, flavor, color, stability, and other characteristics. Before being incorporated into margarine, they must be made crystal clear, practically colorless, tasteless, odorless, and insofar as possible, resistant to deterioration. Four basic steps accomplish these objectives.

First is the refining proper. To the crude oil a caustic soda solution is added in controlled amounts. This neutralizes and removes the components of the oils that are known collectively as free fatty acids and which are ordinarily present in small amounts. Other minor substances also are removed in this manner. One of these is lecithin, a fatty material often used as an anti-spattering agent in margarine formulas.

The oil is then washed by being heated while mixed with hot water, separated, and dried under a vacuum at high temperature. Washing removes any remaining minor impurities left over from the refining step. It is controlled by chemical and physical tests.

As a second step, the refined and washed oil is bleached to remove color that might still be present. One conventional method treats the oil for a short time with small amounts of bleaching earth and charcoal, under vacuum and at elevated temperatures. After this conditioning has absorbed the color bodies, the bleaching mixture is filtered from the oil. Oils may differ from batch to batch in their bleaching requirements and the purposes for which they are being prepared. Margarine oils must be limpid, pure, and brilliant.

The third stage is hardening the oil so that it will be plastic or semi-solid at room temperature, or about 75° F. Hardening is a chemical process that has not always been fully understood. Known as "hydrogenation", it consists of adding varying amounts of hydrogen gas to the heated oil while the oil is under pressure in the presence of a very small quantity of a catalyst.

After some agitation, under these conditions, the oil will be "hydrogenated"—that is, the oil will have some hydrogen chemically joined to it. The chemist describes this by saying that hydrogen atoms have linked to some of the carbon atoms in the molecules which make up fats. The physical results are twofold. The oil has become more solid—that is, its melting point has been raised. Also, its resistance to deterioration through oxidation has been improved. Nutritional aspects of hydrogenation are described in Chapter V.

The hydrogenation procedure is a tightly controlled chemical process aimed to secure a fat mixture that will be semi-solid, plastic, or even quite soft and yet will maintain a required consistency over a given range of temperature. It is limited in application. It not only creates the necessary consistency but also helps the keeping quality of the fat. A margarine label may state "partially hardened"—a more exact description than simply "hardened."

Margarines of conventional plastic texture can be formed and packed (at about 50° to 60° F.), keep plastic at home refrigerator temperatures (about 45° F.), and hold their shape and not separate their emulsion for a period of time at normal use temperatures (about 75° to 80° F.). Careful control of the hardening phase is the means by which these qualities are realized.

Not all margarine oils are hardened. In many margarines most of the oils have been so treated, but some may be very lightly hardened or left liquid. Often two or more oils of different degrees of hardness are combined to achieve the desired result. Soft margarines are composed of oils that have not been hardened to the extent of those used in plastic margarines and frequently are blended with a liquid oil.

The treated oil passes through a fourth and last processing step: deodorization, to remove aromas and flavors by putting the oil under high temperature and vacuum. A small amount of steam is injected. Elements lending odor or flavor that are residual in the oil or that are imparted by prior processing are distilled off.

Selecting Fats and Oils

The manufacturer has pre-set criteria for the finished fats and oils he uses. His selection often is made even before their processing is begun or completed.

He uses different formulas which are closely guarded secrets and often are covered by patents. New margarines (and margarine-like spreads) are being tried or experimented on all the time in his laboratories. A few broad types of formulas may be distinguished.

First and most typical are margarines composed of a combination of vegetable oils. An average formula of this type might be 80 percent soybean oil and 20 percent cottonseed oil. A second group is that of margarines composed wholly of a single vegetable oil, which may be soybean oil or (especially in premium or special margarines) corn or safflower oil.

A third group is that of blend margarines which combine animal and vegetable fats in one proportion or another. They are commonly referred to as "AV" or "VA" products, depending on the predominance of animal ("A") or vegetable ("V") fat. The "AV" types are required by the Standards to be between 50 and 90 per cent animal fat. A typical "AV" weight composition would be 90 per cent pure lard and 10 per cent soybean oil.

The fourth and smallest class is that of margarines composed wholly of animal fats. Usually the fat content is slightly hardened pure lard. Until 1969 this type was a very low consumer cost product. In that year government programs resulted in a high price for lard.

Formulas are geared to the cost of the oils, which are the major ingredient cost in margarine. Prices of oils and fats change a good deal, like all commodity prices. A manufacturer may switch oils in order to take advantage of price movements and keep his products' prices down. Some formulas, however, including those of many premium or special margarines are not subject to such adjustments.

Prices for the major margarine ingredients oils are reported through the regular market informational services. Usually they are expressed in terms of prices for crude oil at midwestern or other shipping points. To these prices must be added refining and transport costs. As oil prices change constantly they may not reflect the cost of the fat in a given margarine in the store for the ingredient was purchased some time before and may well have cost more or less than the current prices quoted for it.

Having selected and purchased his refined and prepared ingredient oils (he may be his own refiner), the manufacturer will try to avoid inventory cost by putting them into production promptly. Refined oils are shipped to him most commonly by tank truck, usually holding 40,000 pounds or in rail tank cars containing 60,000 or 150,000 pounds each.

On arrival the oils are laboratory tested and pumped into large storage tanks. Vegetable oils are stored separately from animal fats or mixtures containing such fats. They are not brought together until the actual blending and processing begins.

MANUFACTURE: OILS BLENDING

Manufacture sometimes proceeds by batches as one formula is handled after another, or it may be by continuous flow, often regulated by automatic controls. The first step in the actual manufacture of margarine is to bring together in a pre-designed blend the deodorized fats and oils according to the formula being followed.

The oil blending may have been performed by the refiner or it may be done by the margarine manufacturer on his own premises in the storage tanks or in separate tanks built for that purpose. The warmed oils are pumped from the separate storage tanks in the quantities desired and are stirred. Precise automatic scales usually measure the volume of each type of oil and of the total mix.

The blending stage is also, as a rule, the point at which certain oil-soluble ingredients are added to the oil or fat phase. These are chiefly coloring, vitamins, and emulsifying agents. They did add very little to the weight of the mix, but they start the blend on its way to becoming margarine.

COLORING

Color is one of nature's finest gifts. Consumers expect margarine to be colored to resemble summer butter. The coloration of margarine is part of man's associations of certain colors with certain foods and also of the close relationship between the yellow color and vitamin A in nature.

Margarine is colored by natural or artificial coloring materials. All such colorants must be those approved by the U.S. Food and Drug Administration under the food additives and pure food laws, in particular the color additives law of 1960. All are oil-soluble.

Yellow colorants in nature derive in great part from a group of substances collectively known as carotenoids, the name given to a group of plant pigments. Carotenes themselves are pro-vitamin A, meaning that the body is able to transform them into vitamin A nutrient. Thus they are important in vitamin A nutrition.

Some margarines use natural carotene for coloring. Ordinarily natural carotene is in a prepared concentrated form obtained from carrots, palm oil, or other vegetable sources. It may carry some independent vitamin A value as well as being itself pro-vitamin A.

The leading colorant, however, is a member of the carotene family known as beta carotene. This substance provides the yellow color and possesses the greatest amount of pro-vitamin A activity of all the carotenes.

As commercially prepared, beta carotene is a man-made, concentrated form of carotene made primarily for yellow coloring of margarine and other foods and acting secondarily as a vitamin A fortification agent. The desired shade of yellow results when standardized beta carotene is incorporated into the oils to provide a vitamin A value per pound of finished margarine that is at some point between 5,000 and 5,500 units. The rest of the required vitamin A is added directly.

A third source of coloring employed in some margarines is derived in part from the tropical annatto plant. The coating of the seed contains a substance called bixin which is widely used as a purified extract in food coloring. It may be combined with a stabilizer.

The color shade of most margarines—really a light combination of yellows and reds—is measured by an instrument named the tintometer. Margarines marketed in some regions may be colored more deeply than those for distribution elsewhere.

The South seems to prefer a darker tinge than does the Northeast, where a light shade is most often favored.

The chore of home coloring margarine has virtually disappeared, and with it the one-time capsule of coloring matter or the "squeeze bag" package. Uncolored table margarine is sold to a limited extent where a special tax makes the colored product cost more. Bulk margarine made for bakery use is often uncolored.

VITAMINS

Fortification of American margarine with vitamin A is universal for the retail consumer product. It is accomplished by the addition of vitamin A or its esters (synthetic vitamin A acetate and palmitate). When beta carotene or natural carotene are used as coloring agents, as described above, they also contribute part of the vitamin A value, and so fortification is performed by a combination of agents.

Vitamin A is an optional ingredient under the Standards. If fortified—and all table margarine and some industrial margarines are fortified with this vitamin—the minimum level must be 15,000 U.S.P. (or I.U.) units per pound. Generally manufacturers increase this slightly in order to ensure that the minimum will be present at the time of consumer purchase.

A fortification preparation commonly used consists of a balanced ratio of synthetic beta carotene and of vitamin A. The former provides about a third of the vitamin and the latter the remainder. Pure beta carotene is a brownish-red crystalline powder with an equivalency of 1,670,000 U.S.P units of vitamin A per gram. For the purpose of margarine manufacture it is used in a vegetable oil solution.

Some margarines are fortified also with vitamin D. When this vitamin is added, it is in an amount to provide a minimum of 2,000 U.S.P units per pound—although this level is not specifically set by any standard.

American margarine, unlike many margarines in Europe, is not fortified with vitamin E. This vitamin, however, is naturally present to some extent in the vegetable oils in margarine.

Emulsifiers

The fats and oils are now ready for combination with the liquid phase to form the important water-in-oil emulsion described earlier in this chapter. To help the water and oil cling together as they should, emulsifying agents are incorporated into the blend. Added in very small amounts they tend to reduce the surface tension between the water droplets and the oil particles. Without the emulsifiers the water and oil would tend to separate, no matter how thoroughly they have been mixed.

Emulsifiers therefore stabilize but certain emulsifiers perform other services. Some help the margarine to melt evenly in the cooking pan without undue sticking. One—lecithin—helps proper browning in the pan and reduces the natural tendency of the emulsion to spatter the fat when heated to cooking temperature.

The Standards permit the optional use of certain natural and commonly used emulsifiers. Those chiefly employed are lecithin and the glycerine derivatives of fatty acids called monoglycerides (the latter contain diglycerides as a diluent). They may be added singly or in combination to a maximum of one half of one per cent of the finished product's weight, although lecithin and the monoglycerides may each be up to that level if they are used together.

All these ingredients are officially approved food additives. Lecithin is a natural fat substance derived from soybean oil. It is found in living cells as a surface active agent, much as it is used in margarine, and is a component of eggs and other foods. Lecithin can be added directly to the margarine oils; it helps the product's cooking capability and its palatability. The monoglycerides and diglycerides are all products of fats and are really special types of fat. Generally they originate from the same type of oil found in the margarine blend. Specialized preparations of these emulsifiers and their variations have been tailored for margarine use.

Other ingredients may be added to the blended oils, including certain flavoring agents. More commonly, however, such other ingredients enter into the product through the liquid phase.

LIQUID PHASE

Approximately 16 to 18 per cent of margarine is liquid—the second largest volume component.

Traditionally, and most commonly at present, this liquid part is simply skim milk. The Standards permit the use of such milk in fluid form or as a dry powder (nonfat dry milk) reconstituted with water. They also allow whole milk, cream, buttermilk, soy milk, or soybean milk or water. In all regular or standard margarines the water content is limited; in low-fat margarine it is the leading ingredient.

Most margarines utilize skim milk (or nonfat dry milk) in the powder form. Manufactured by the spray or instant-drying methods, it is reconstituted at the margarine plant. Its price is government-supported. In 1969 the average cost was 25 cents a pound. The Standards require that the milk solids in reconstituted skim milk be equivalent to 10 per cent of the weight of the water. If dried buttermilk is reconstituted, the solids minimum is 8½ per cent of the resultant blend.

Milk solids contain protein and other nutrients. They comprise about 1.5 per cent of the finished margarine's weight. When whole milk or cream is incorporated a small amount of milk fat is thereby added.

Soybean milk, a preparation of finely crushed soybeans and water, is employed in margarines prepared for vegetarian, or kosher or other dietary purposes. The solids proportion is the same as in nonfat milk. The low-fat or diet margarines frequently use water in place of milk. The ingredients statement on the package identifies by name the milk or other liquid phase used.

Milk received at the margarine plant almost always has been pasteurized, but as a precaution is re-pasteurized to destroy any bacteria. Liquid milk is never stored very long at the factory. Tests are made to assure that the dry milk meets the requirements of both trade and official standards, and that the liquid

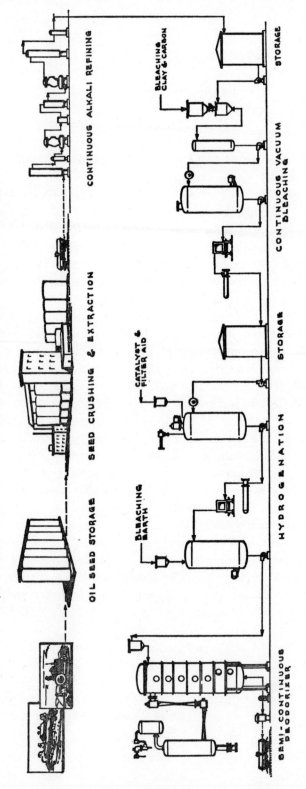

PREPARATION OF MARGARINE FATS & OILS

OIL SEED STORAGE

SEED CRUSHING & EXTRACTION

CONTINUOUS ALKALI REFINING

BLEACHING CLAY & CARBON

STORAGE

CONTINUOUS VACUUM BLEACHING

CATALYST & FILTER AID

STORAGE

HYDROGENATION

BLEACHING EARTH

SEMI-CONTINUOUS DEODORIZER

COURTESY OF VOTATOR DIVISION, CHEMETRON CORPORATION

MARGARINE MANUFACTURING PROCESS

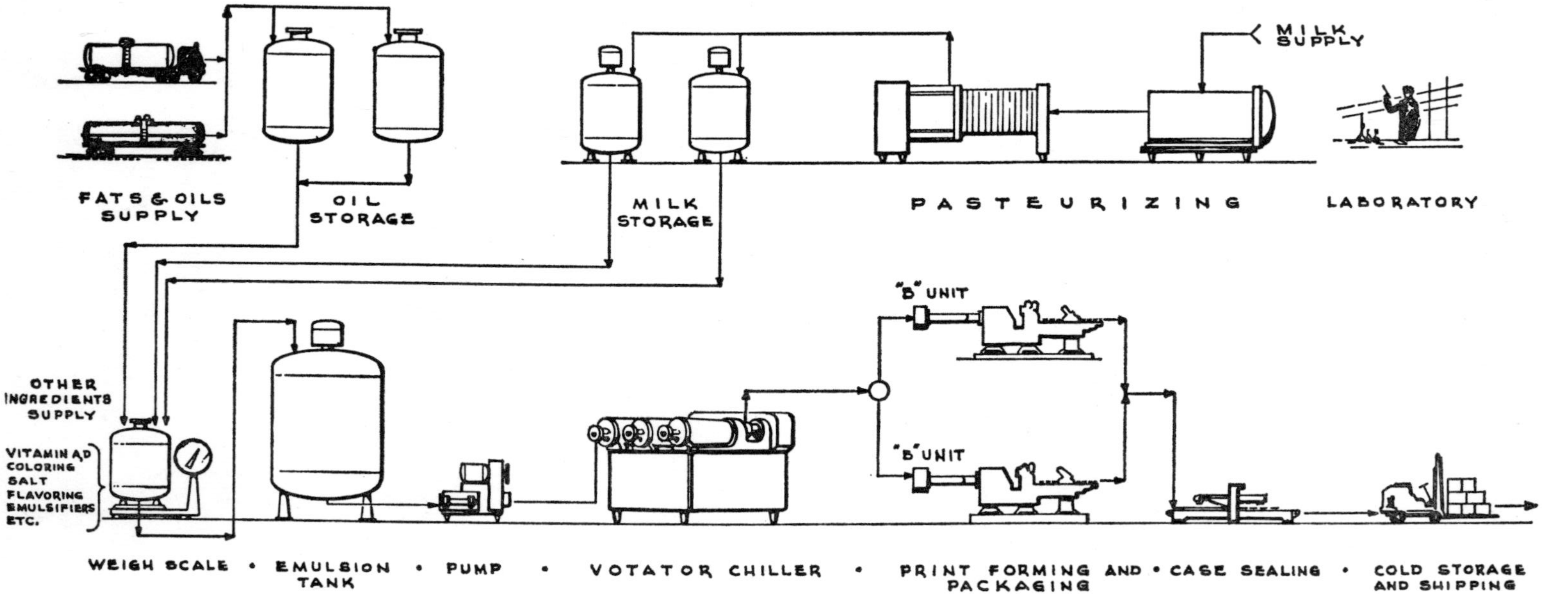

MILK SUPPLY

LABORATORY

PASTEURIZING

MILK STORAGE

OIL STORAGE

FATS & OILS SUPPLY

OTHER INGREDIENTS SUPPLY

VITAMIN A D
COLORING
SALT
FLAVORING
EMULSIFIERS
ETC.

"B" UNIT

"B" UNIT

VOTATOR CHILLER

PRINT FORMING AND PACKAGING

CASE SEALING AND SHIPPING

COLD STORAGE AND SHIPPING

WEIGH SCALE • EMULSION TANK • PUMP • VOTATOR CHILLER • PRINT FORMING AND • CASE SEALING • COLD STORAGE
PACKAGING • AND SHIPPING

COURTESY OF VOTATOR DIVISION CHEMETRON CORPORATION

milk, reconstituted or not, is of the right purity, acidity, and
specific gravity and without unwanted flavors and odors. It
must be as uniform as possible, with low acidity. All the containing or handling equipment is, of course, sterilized regularly.

FLAVOR

Today's consumer is discriminating. She expects margarine
to convey a flavor as inviting as that of the best butter taste
she knows. Also her taste may be that of a region which likes
this flavor stronger or milder than others prefer. Most margarine makers aim for the light yet sharp flavor of ripened
milk from which dairy butter is made.

This is accomplished by handling the milk in a manner similar
to that of butter making, and by means of flavor agents or
enhancers. The flavor must be created—it cannot be derived
from the oils, or, as in butter, from the milk. This necessity
results in an advantage. Brands differ in flavor, but the
flavor of a particular brand can be kept uniform and therefore
dependable barring problems arising during shipment or in
store handling.

In the milk flavoring process, selected micro-organisms are
grown in small batches of pasteurized milk. After about five
to fifteen hours these bacteria induce a chemical change whereby lactic acid and certain flavor-containing and aromatic compounds are generated, just as in the process of making butter.
The ripened or cultured milk is then used to flavor milk going
into the margarine. More and more frequently the flavoring is
accomplished by adding to the liquid phase diacetyl, a substance produced by the ripening process. Other flavoring agents
may be used that are derived from butterfat and function with
the fat rather than the milk or water. The amount is very
small.

All flavor agents used in margarine are named by the Standards
as optional ingredients. When the flavor of a margarine is
produced in any part by the addition of one of the substances
named, and not from the ripening alone, the label will say

"artificially flavored" even though cultured milk may be included.

SALT

Americans like their margarine salted, a preference supposed to go back to the days when salting was the main method of preserving butter. Salt in margarine serves a double purpose: it lends a flavor that is desired, and acts as a moderate preservative.

The salt must be of the best food quality, according to the manufacturer's or trade specifications for fineness and cleanliness. Running from one and a half to three percent of the total, salt usually ranks as the third-place component in weight. Its crystals are completely dissolved in the milk or water. Unsalted or low sodium margarines are made without any salt, principally for special dietary purposes.

PRESERVATIVES

Margarine's flavor and its water-in-oil makeup call for protective measures to keep quality intact against natural oxidizing and other influences. The best keeping qualities are not unlimited and modern margarines are sensitive to heat and exposure.

For the consumer this means that the product should be refrigerated and should be used within a reasonable time after purchase. For the manufacturer it means that the product he offers must be able to withstand ordinary physical and temperature strains within a total distribution period of up to six or eight weeks, or even more. (In actuality, it is often closer to three or four weeks and sometimes less.) Since proper refrigeration may not be available all through this period, the Standards permit the utilization of certain preservatives in addition to the salt. These substances are all stated on the label by specific name. They are regulated under the pure food laws and their use in food processing is well-established.

Many margarines use the familiar preservative, sodium ben-

zoate. It is incorporated in the liquid phase and is permitted
in amounts up to one-tenth of one per cent of the total product
weight. Its chief function is to protect the margarine from
the molds or yeasts which may occur in foods. Because sodium
benzoate may not act as effectively in margarines with less
cultured milk content, other preservatives are also allowed by
the Standards. Some margarines employ potassium sorbate
which is permitted in margarine to a maximum of one-tenth
of one per cent.

A special class of substances has been recognized as helpful
in protecting the ingredient oils from developing undesirable
flavors. It has been noted that the hydrogenation process helps
keeping quality. Some manufacturers use the permitted protective agent calcium disodium EDTA which acts to neutralize
or sequester possible trace elements of minerals. It is used up
to 75 parts per million. Natural isopropyl citrate or stearyl
citrate are other protective agents that may be incorporated
in the oils within extremely small maximum amounts.

All of these protective ingredients are permitted under the
federal food additives law. All are specifically named in the
statement of ingredients on the package, together with an indication of their purpose, and all play roles secondary to good
quality materials, correct processes, protective packaging, and
refrigeration.

Completing the Margarine

The oil and milk phases, prepared and ready, are brought
together in a rapid blending operation which takes place in
stainless steel vats or closed vessels into which the two prepared
components are pumped. Often this is accomplished by automatic equipment that measures exact proportions.

Warmed by the moderately heated oil phase the blend is
kept at about 100° F. while being continuously stirred at fairly
high speed. The swirling smooth yellow mix becomes the final
assembled emulsion in its last liquid stage. The ingredients are
evenly distributed by the action, much as is done with some
mixtures in a home blender in the kitchen.

As soon as the dispersion is accomplished, the warm mix is pumped into the next stage where it undergoes transformation from liquid to the desired consistency of plastic mass or solid by means of quick chilling and crystallization (or "congealing and working" as the Standard refers to it). The liquid emulsion thereby becomes more or less solid according to the type of margarine being produced.

In perhaps nine-tenths of American production this is done by means of the Votator system. A significant improvement in margarine technology introduced in 1936, the system moves the blend in a continuous flow within a closed system under very precise controls.

The blend enters the first part (or "A" unit) of the votator chiller at a temperature of about 90° to 100° F. As it passes through three chromeplated tubes, it is successively and rapidly cooled within one or two minutes to 45° or 50° F. The tubes combine a heat exchanger with a mixing mechanism. The solidifying mix is agitated, losing its heat as it is propelled into contact with the cold surface of the tube.

Within about two minutes the mix is pumped into a second ("B") unit. This is another tube-like device in which the mix undergoes brief intervals of rest and movement. The effect is to temper the blend and enable proper crystallization of the chilled crystals of fat to develop.

Soft margarines are treated so as to modify the solidification. Whipped margarines also are prepared by means of a special blending procedure in which a pure inert gas, usually nitrogen, is added to the mix to increase its volume. Liquid margarines also receive special blending to enable the mix to remain in its liquid state.

Some American manufacturers continue to prefer other systems which are more commonly used in Europe, such as the once-popular process of congealing the margarine mix on a large chilled drum. When this method is employed for regular, plastic margarine, the congealed blend crystallizes during a controlled working period.

These manufacturing procedures are subject to some individual modification by the manufacturer. They are as critical to quality and uniformity of the finished margarine as are the fat and milk preparation stages. Numerous checks or tests are made along the entire production line to ensure such characteristics as proper fat content, correct weight, flavor and coloring, vitamin potency, and texture.

PACKAGING

The completed margarine is drawn from the crystallization stage at a temperature of about 50° to 60° F. It is immediately formed into its finished shape and placed in unit containers by automatic equipment. There are different makes and styles of forming equipment. Regular margarines in quarter-pound units may be formed and packaged at rates of 2,500 to 3,500 pounds an hour; solid one-pound units at rates up to 4,500 pounds an hour. Soft margarines are turned out at a slower rate.

The forming machine receives the margarine and shapes it into the familiar quarter-pound sticks or other sizes. These are wrapped as they pass through a fast automatic machine. The wrapping is usually protective aluminum foil or oil-resistant parchment, or waxed paper.

Retail cartons are of paperboard of specified weight and strength to protect the contents. The outer covering bearing the label may be laminated to the box or applied as an overwrap. Printed paraffined cartons are also used.

Soft margarines are poured into stiff aluminum or plastic tubs which are lidded and, if half-pound, over-wrapped with a paperboard sleeve that serves the purpose of an outer carton. Soft margarines also are available in one-pound bowls without an overwrap. Liquid margarines are sold in plastic bottles.

One-pound solid prints and half-pound units, circular or rectangular in shape, are customarily packaged only in heavy parchment or waxed paper. Margarine is also prepared in individual servings or "pats" for use in public eating places. These are rectangular pieces or—to meet one federal requirement— triangular. Such "pats" are generally prepared in slightly less than one-fourth ounce weights, or 72 pats to the pound, but may be smaller or larger. They often carry an individual protective waxed paper covering bearing the name "Margarine" and are packed in cartons of five to ten pounds.

Margarine for retail sale is shipped in heavy corrugated paperboard containers. Most of these contain thirty pounds but some are in twenty-four pound, twelve pound or other sizes. Thus triply or doubly enclosed, freshly made retail margarine is put into cold storage to "set" and is then shipped.

Bulk or industrial margarine for institutions and bakers is packaged in solid quantities ranging from thirty to five hundred pounds, in heavy boxes, tins, or steel drums.

The package sizes in which margarine is sold are subject to federal and various state laws and regulations. Labeling and weight laws and regulations for margarines are described in Chapter VI. Different lots of margarine are identified by a code so that the manufacturer can identify the formula and production time of the product if that becomes necessary.

THE INDUSTRY

The manufacture of margarine is accomplished with a relatively small industry. A limited number of factories can turn out a large quantity of the product. In 1969 the industry numbered some 56 plants, owned and operated by 34 different business firms. A 1963 census reported that the industry added $58 million of value and paid nearly $15 million in wages. These levels have since been well exceeded. A list of margarine manufacturers is supplied in the Appendix.

Since 1950 the industry has probably increased capacity by as much as 50 per cent. Margins over costs have been low as the record of average consumer prices demonstrates.

Production volume is variable. A hundred million pounds a year is a substantial operation. A minority, perhaps seven or eight firms, exceed that. About six middle-size volume firms are estimated to be below this level. The rest are smaller producers and, in several cases, small businesses. (In 1969 some Wisconsin creameries produced a butter-vegetable oil spread legally defined as margarine.)

Production leadership is not consistent with firm size. While most of the largest producers are publicly-owned corporations, some are privately owned, and some of the corporate manufacturers are smaller quantity producers.

In 1969 the average number of plants operated per enterprise came to about one and a half. The range extended from the 16 firms having a single plant to two firms having five or more plants. The largest producer does not appear to account for more than 18 per cent of the entire consumer market. One report in 1966 assigned 46 per cent of the market to the four largest producers.[2] Some manufacturers specialize in their own brands; others in margarines carrying the labels of retail distributors.

Margarine manufacturing is a part of the food processing industry. There has been significant integration with other food manufacturing, including dairy processing. Most of the larger-volume manufacturers and some of the smaller ones manufacture other food products. Thirteen own or are affiliated with vegetable oil refining establishments. Production plants cluster about major metropolitan areas, yet several plants are also successful in small towns.

The intensity of competition between manufacturers is fostered by the product's intrinsic appeal to price and by the competitive nature of the fats and oils industry in all its branches. To this must be added the influence of the large retail distributors, whose bargaining strength is large and who select the brands they will offer their customers.

1. Useful technical descriptions of margarine manufacture and related fats and oils technology are: Karl F. Mattil, "Butter and Margarine," in Daniel Swern, ed. *Bailey's Industrial Oil and Fat Products* (New York, 3rd ed., 1964); G. B. Crump, "The Technology of Margarine Manufacture," in R. T. Holman, *et al.*, eds., *Progress in the Chemistry of Fats and Other Lipids* (New York, 1958); A. J. C. Andersen and P. N. Williams, *Margarine* (New York, 2nd rev. ed., 1965); and M. K. Schwitzer, *Margarine and Other Fats* (New York, 1956). The latter two works are more detailed than the first two. A useful survey is "U. S. Edible Fats and Oils Refining Capacity, 1967" in the U. S.

Department of Agriculture's *Fats and Oils Situation,* No. FOS-244 (Washington, September, 1968), 24-34.

2. National Commission on Food Marketing, *The Structure of Food Manufacturing* (Washington, 1968), 75.

"The Man Who Got Wise"
(Advertising and Selling, April 1912)

IV

Distribution to Consumers

If that cornucopia of living, the bulging brown grocery bag, contains any representative assortment of foods as it is carried out of the store, the chances are good that a table spread will be among them. The greater likelihood is that the spread will be margarine.

Table spread has a traditional place in the national food shopping list. Consumption of it has reversed the former predominance of butter and brought margarine into top place. The vegetable spread has mostly, but not completely, overcome the decline in butter sales. Table spread consumption averages per person a little less than it did a generation ago. This probably is the result of different influences, including the decreasing use of spread-using bread and potatoes and the increased consumption of such foods as peanut butter, mayonnaise, and snacks.

Margarine has been a striking instance of consumer movement into an alternate food when a traditional food could not meet consumer supply and price requirements. Consumption has been strengthened qualitatively by the introduction of new types of margarines, moving away from some traditional butter characteristics.

The gross consumption of margarine is visible from the rising annual production figures (Table I, Appendix). Refinements of consumption and use information are more difficult. This section presents the subject on the basis of available information, including government reports, past surveys, and estimates. A comprehensive story of margarine distribution, purchase, and utilization by consumers is not feasible in this space nor is it possible in the light of available information. A profile may be obtained, however, from the different approaches discussed in this chapter.

PER PERSON AND HOUSEHOLD

Per capita average national consumption is the simple measurement established by dividing the population figure by that reported for a product's total disappearance into domestic distribution channels, including loss through waste or spoilage. It is a helpful benchmark.

The per capita figure discloses that in 1969 total production of margarine was the equivalent of 10.8 pounds per person (product weight; the fat content would be 8.6 pounds). Table III in the Appendix shows margarine and butter per capita consumption for many years back. It indicates a dramatic margarine upturn following a low point of 2.3 pounds in 1939.

The per capita chart also reveals that margarine has increased its volume available per person by roughly four times in thirty years and has been rising almost annually, outpacing the rapid population growth of the postwar years. One forecast is that it will be at or near 13 pounds per person average consumption in 1980. That would mean an increase of about one-fourth in total consumption during the nineteen-seventies.

During the nineteen-fifties an unusual increase of 70 per cent stemmed from the legalization of colored margarine and the appearance of new products. The nineteen-sixties showed an increase of 25 per cent. Any forecast must allow for changes in living styles in our rapidly changing society and in the composition of the population. Everything considered, however, the 13 pounds projection is an acceptable one.

Per capita information is obviously useful as a yardstick for gross national measurement. It tells nothing of the important variables between people, groups, and places. Many Americans are consuming more than the 10.8 pounds a year. That average in turn would average about ½ ounce a day — roughly two to three small pats. Others, of course, eat less.

Some idea of the variations is gained from well-known

POUNDS OF FATS AND OILS USED PER HOUSEHOLD PER WEEK

SPRING 1965 AND 1955*

Region	Total Fats And Oils		Table Fats				Cooking Fats				Salad and Cooking Oils		Salad Dressings	
			Margarine		Butter		Lard		Vegetable					
	1965	1955	1965	1955	1965	1955	1965	1955	1965	1955	1965	1955	1965	1955
U. S.	2.70	2.97	0.80	0.66	0.42	0.67	0.26	0.47	0.34	0.46	0.36	0.19	0.53	0.51
N. E.	2.45	2.44	.66	.61	.57	.77	.13	.13	.17	.29	.46	.24	.46	.39
N. Cen.	2.62	2.90	.80	.62	.55	.83	.17	.32	.33	.47	.26	.13	.50	.53
South	3.09	3.54	.87	.68	.21	.46	.50	1.04	.52	.59	.39	.18	.60	.59
West	2.42	2.91	.84	.79	.35	.58	.09	.19	.26	.49	.32	.27	.55	.58

* Derived from U. S. Department of Agriculture, *Food Consumption of Households in the United States, Spring 1965* (Washington, 1967); id., *Food Consumption of Households in the United States . . . 1955* (Washington, 1957). The 1955 figures have been adjusted to be comparable to the 1965 report's family level of three.

government reports on household consumption of foods during a test period in each of the years 1955 and 1965. They confirm the growth of margarine use, reporting it at 21 per cent between the two years. More significantly they show the spread's consumption has been growing in each one of the four major regions covered.

The tabulation on page 50 is taken from these reports but is drawn up to compare the margarine figures with those for other food fats.

The household surveys disclose that families living in the

"In accordance with Title 6, Section 8, Chapter 8 of the laws of this state, I wish to announce that I am serving oleomargarine." (Gourmet Magazine.)

South (traditionally a strong margarine-consuming region) maintain a higher consumption level than do those elsewhere. A striking ten-year increase in all regions is revealed. Families living in smaller cities and towns generally are among the largest users. Suburbia, with many younger middle-class families, has become a major consumer area and may be largely responsible for the 1955-65 consumption increases reported in most metropolitan areas.

Other geographical consumption information is available from various surveys. It presents the familiar picture of increasing acceptance and consumption but is often too generalized to take into account the very different situations that exist in food habits and use throughout the country.

Two surveys in the mid-sixties have some pertinent interest in this connection. One portrays consumers in large metropolitan areas as consuming less than the national average per capita amount. For some cities this can be partially explained by the large proportion of the butter supply that is consumed in such centers, especially in restaurants, and partly by food tastes and eating patterns derived from ethnic groups or countries where margarine is not as familiar as it is in the United States. Another report found the same below average consumption rate for farm families. This finding may be compared to the frequency with which rural storekeepers have testified to margarine purchases by their farm family customers. In sum, the geographical picture of margarine use is a rather variable one.

A special insight is gained by looking at consumption rates of margarines and butter by certain geographical areas, as afforded by data on the division of margarine and butter sales by marketing areas in comparison with similar divisions of population and all commodity grocery sales. This is done for 1969 in the table and map on pages 54-55. Noteworthy is the importance of margarine in the east central, southeast, and southwest areas, relative to population, whereas butter is most important to relative population in northeast areas. These are of course not comparisons of absolute volumes or of per capita consumption rates.

FOOD STORE SALES OF TABLE SPREAD, 1958-1969

(MILLIONS OF POUNDS)

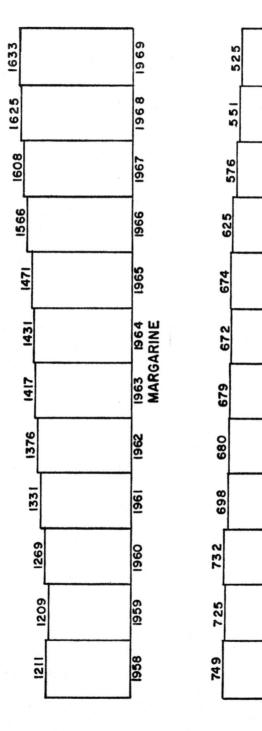

MARGARINE

1958	1959	1960	1961	1962	1963	1964	1965	1966	1967	1968	1969
1211	1209	1269	1331	1376	1417	1431	1471	1566	1608	1625	1633

BUTTER

1958	1959	1960	1961	1962	1963	1964	1965	1966	1967	1968	1969
749	725	732	698	680	679	672	674	625	576	551	525

DIVISION BY AREAS OF THE TOTAL 1969 STORE SALES OF
MARGARINE, BUTTER, AND ALL GROCERY COMMODITIES,
AND OF POPULATION

Area	Division of Population	Division of 1969 Store Sales Margarine	Butter	All Commodity
New England	5.7	5.4	9.8	6.4
Metro New York	8.2	4.0	12.3	7.8
Middle Atlantic	11.5	10.9	18.3	11.9
East Central	16.2	18.1	16.1	16.2
Metro Chicago	3.8	3.6	5.1	4.1
West Central	13.8	14.9	14.9	12.5
Southeast	16.1	17.2	5.7	15.3
Southwest	10.2	9.8	2.3	9.2
Metro Los Angeles	4.8	5.0	4.7	5.8
Remaining Pacific	9.7	11.2	10.8	10.8

(Courtesy of the A. C. Nielsen Company)

The available breakdown by income classes is more explicit.
Margarine has made gains in all income classes but, apparently,
chiefly in the broad spectrum of the middle class. It is commonly found in the home refrigerator of middle and upper income homes. In the age of affluence it has become a rather typical American food, leaving behind the old epithet of "poor
man's spread." (Paradoxically, very low income families are
often said to buy butter and the federal government disposes of
much of its surplus butter to persons on relief rolls or otherwise
not active consumers.) The 1965 survey found that families in
the $3,000 to $9,000 annual income brackets were heaviest
users, but that the difference in this respect between income
groups was not sharp. At each end of the income range—the
poor and the well to do—margarine use tapered off from the
middle group highs.

Age groups also differ in their use of the spread. One source
states that margarine is bought by the "young middle" families
with parents between thirty and forty years of age. With the
prospect of younger people forming a larger share of the population, the importance of this group's consumption is manifest.
Another statement is that some 85 per cent of all families used
margarine in 1967, apparently half of them buying it is their
only table spread.

POPULATION AND TABLE SPREAD SALES IN FOOD STORES, 1969

POPULATION 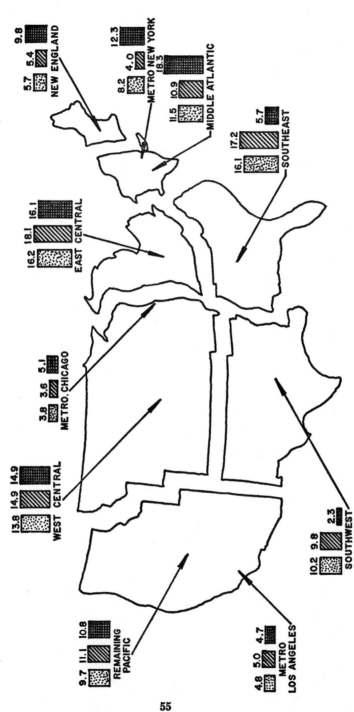   MARGARINE PURCHASES   BUTTER PURCHASES

Courtesy of the A. C. Nielsen Company. The geographical divisions are those of the Nielsen Food and Drug Territories. Pennsylvania is split between Atlantic and East Central, and Virginia between Atlantic (counties adjacent to D.C.) and Southeast.

55

A Distribution Profile

Consumers buy margarine principally in food stores but much
is purchased through other channels. Most is bought in one-
pound packages, but there are other sizes. Consumers buy
more plastic or regular margarine than any other type, as
described in the opening chapter, but other product types are
important too.

A profile of major sales channels, package sizes, and product
types in distribution is estimated for 1969 in the following
table. It is constructed from production data and private
estimates.[1] Although the figures are not rounded they are not
intended to provide precise volumes—being mostly estimates—
but rather to show relationships. Indirectly it offers yet another
view of consumer buying decisions.

Class	Estimated Million Lbs. (1969)	Approximate Percent of Total Distribution
Total distribution	2180	100%
One-pound—	1953	89
In stores:	1823	83
Regular or plastic	1383	63
Soft	320	15
Whipped and diet	120	5
Non-store:	130	6
Milk routes, etc.	100	5
Government procurement	30	1
Half-pound (chiefly in stores)—	53	2
"Pats" for eating places—	21	1
Industrial (bulk)—	173	8

In recent years all the above classes of margarine have shown
consumption increases. Most notable has been expansion in the
use of soft margarine. Another increase has taken place in
sales to restaurants, a distinct category that does not show in
the table because many eating places purchase margarine in
retail or bulk packages. It is estimated that at least 100 million

pounds of margarine were consumed in public eating places in 1969, including the 21 million pounds of pre-made individual servings called "pats", "chiplets" or "reddies."

The figures presented in the above tabulation are not intended to be exact. Necessarily they are rounded in order to adjust to production data and to reach a consensus between government-reported production and information from other sources. The profile, however, is probably a fairly accurate one of how margarine goes into distribution and consumption.

CONSUMER ACCEPTANCE

Predictably, margarine emerges as a popular food in the wide consumer class that is middle-income family America. It would be interesting to know more about margarine buying decisons. That acceptance is well established and growing is a truism. What constitutes this acceptance is a matter of more or less informed opinion.

One view is that consumers have simply become accustomed to margarine. Many of those who were children during World War II, when many families transferred from butter to the more available spread, have grown up with a preference for its flavor and texture and without any of the old prejudices about it. Another view ties this in with urbanization and the concommittant changes in life styles that stress casual, informal eating and do not put a status symbol on butter.

Yet another explanation is that today's consumer is more sophisticated about margarine as a nutritious table spread which costs less and offers a variety of choices and features such as soft texture. The interest of many consumers in poly-unsaturated foods is cited as a further contributory factor. Doubtless these influences all have played a part in creating today's consumer acceptance pattern or patterns involving margarine. Doubtless, too, the very basic effect of the ascending cost of living—of which butter's price is often seen as an exemplar—has had its effect.

The uses to which margarine is put in the home are not

precisely known although some private surveys cover the subject. From available information it appears that most families buying margarine use it for a spread as well as cooking or seasoning. The indications are that its use as a spread has increased, partly as a result of the newer premium margarines. One report in 1965 stated that nearly two-thirds of the consuming families used margarine as a spread, while nearly a fourth used it as an ingredient of foods prepared in the kitchen and a sixth as a cooking or seasoning agent.

It is likely that a greater volume is used in the home for cooking than as a table spread. Obviously the quantities demanded by cooking for an average family would be well above those consumed as a spread. However, the spread use has certainly increased absolutely and proportionately in recent years. This has been aided by the reduction in home use of butter and by the emphasis some put on margarine for nutritional reasons.

Indeed, margarine's potential in the spread field at home may be less affected in the foreseeable future by butter than by peanut butter, mayonnaise, fruit spreads and similar foods. In restaurants margarine use as a spread has a very great potential, and one that as yet is not well developed.

BRANDS

Consumers see brand indentification on practically all margarine packages. The brand name is the manufacturer's or distributor's way of establishing consumer loyalty. Indirectly it is a kind of grading system, for a consumer who prefers the qualities of a certain brand will look for its name. Brand names also serve an important function in marketing and product innovation by assisting the sale of a margarine through advertising or by the sharing of a well-established name.

Margarine, like many other foods, is offered at retail to the consumer in two large brand divisions. Proprietary brands (sometimes called house or name brands) are those bearing the manufacturer's own brand (usually copyrighted) and also his name and address as the producer. There are two broad sub-groups—the premium brands and the regular brands. The second main division is comprised of store brands.

Premium brands are offered as the best quality margarines, or as margarines with special oils composition or high poly-unsaturate ratios. Their retail prices in 1969 ranged between 40 and 48 cents per pound. (These prices do not include the special margarine taxes imposed by a few states.)

"Regular" brands are offered as good quality margarines, some with compositional features, but as a rule not with the same features of premiums. Their 1969 retail price range was about 29 to 38 cents.

Store brands are those margarines made to bear the brand label of retail distributors and usually carry a distributor's name. Hence they are often called private label brands. The retailer displays his own brands side by side with proprietary brands; his investment does not reflect the advertising or research costs involved in the latter. A variation is the "controlled" brand, which is one owned by a manufacturer but sold for distribution by a single retailer in an area.

It is not uncommon for these margarines to be sold as loss leaders to attract customers. In any event, store brands ordinarily are priced below the proprietary brands and are manufactured with that purpose in mind. They do not carry the selling cost of house brands. In 1969 the prices of store brands tended to be around 19 to 24 cents a pound.

One report on 1967 store turnover indicates that consumption of proprietary brands was about 56 per cent of total margarine sales. The share of store brands was about 44 per cent. In recent years the newer premium margarines are reported to have gained more than the store brands. A cross-section for a period of several weeks in 1969 showed proprietaries to have 60 per cent of retail sales (premiums, 34 per cent; regulars 26 per cent) and store and controlled brands 40 per cent.[2]

Margarine includes a fairly wide range of prices and brands as well as of types, although special types tend to be in the upper classifications. All margarines have two things in com-

mon: they are made within the framework of the Standard as
a minimum floor of quality, and are all priced below the cost
of butter. Each margarine, however, must compete in one of
the three classes.

One of the arresting things about the product's development
has been its occupation of different product and price levels.
This has been a function of its flexibility of manufacture and
also of its facility as a marketed product which offers the consumer table spread choices that previously did not exist. It
was a response to the competitive environment of the supermarket. At the same time, the product's retail prices did not
follow the general rise in the food cost index after 1950—a
unique happening in the food field.

Consumers often wish to know which margarine they should
buy. The answer lies in what the individual person wants in a
table spread, what brand she has found most satisfactory, and
what price she is willing to pay for this part of her food buying.
Many consumers buy margarine and other foods on a price basis.
They are well advised to shop for a margarine they find satisfactory at the lowest available price and to take advantage of
store specials.

Many others base their buying decisions on other factors,
including a learned preference for a given brand's flavor or
other qualities or a preference for a given oil or composition.
It all comes down to the personal equation: what the consumer as an individual finds best for her needs. To help her
selection she will find margarine one of the most fully labeled
food products in terms of ingredients. One study of grocery
stocks in 1968 found 39 per cent of the customers refused to
accept a substitute brand of margarine.[3]

From the marketing standpoint margarine brand diversity
exists because of the great differences in consumer wants or
tastes that can be fulfilled by enlarging the field of choice. The
success of soft margarine is an illustration of how a sound innovation can meet a consumer want

MARKETING

Proprietary premium brand names with national or good regional distribution number probably about twenty or twenty-five. A manufacturer's group of such margarines—regular, soft, corn oil and so forth—often carry the same brand name. The leadership role in marketing played by premium brands and their innovation is far beyond the number of names.

Regular brands are more numerous and store brands are in the hundreds, perhaps as many as 1,500. The margarine brand pool is large for a single food.

The introduction of new margarine types and features has been going on for many years and can be traced back to fundamental events such as the first all-vegetable margarine, the first fortified margarine, and so forth. Many innovations have proved to be failures, sometimes intrinsically and sometimes from a lack of marketing organization or inadequate promotion. Many consist of new ingredient formulas. The more important firsts since World War II have been softer texture, foil wrapping (1956), butter content (1956), whipped (1957), higher polyunsaturate ratio or content (1957-59), liquid corn oil (1958), safflower oil (1961), flavor substances (1962), diet (1964), and soft and liquid (1965). Margarine-like spreads with fruit flavors have also appeared. So have half-and-half butter and vegetable oil margarines.

Margarine product progress received a definite advance as a result of the national sampling that occurred when many consumers turned to the spread during the depression and World War II. When colored margarine was legalized nationally (1943-53), a new national market opened to the spread. It became more feasible to invest in improvements. Butter's support price offered a shelter. Innovation has become an integral part of margarine production and marketing. The proprietary brands will continue to introduce new margarines.

A genuinely new margarine is not easy to design—it is even less easily established with consumers. The preparatory work includes compositional research and product and market test-

ing.[4] The new product must be identified to the ultimate
buyer—the housewife or person who does the shopping—for
the supermarket will not, of its own initiative, make room for
it. Communication therefore is direct between the sponsor of
the new spread, the manufacturer, and the public.

This entails marketing and advertising programs. Margarine
advertising expenditures change from year to year, but in 1969
are estimated to have reached approximately $33 million. As
with many products, complementary programs may include
initiatory offers, special merchandising, and auxiliary aids such
as coupons, premiums, tie-ins, and display management. An
effective promotion is an intelligent one that communicates useful consumer information.

Most margarine advertising relates to premium brands. The
marketing objective may be to launch a new margarine or it
may be to keep an existing one visible and to make its attributes better known. The principal medium, television, may ab-
sorb about three-fourths of the total industry's promotional
outlays. Second in expenditure is advertising in mass media
magazines. Newspaper advertising is a low third.

Promotion is a long-established aspect of margarine which has
always had to win a place away from butter or, later, to compete with peer margarines. The inventor's first product in 1874
was backed by a promotional leaflet and soon there developed
themes of flavor, nourishment, and economy. Nutrition began
to be stressed in the 1930's when vitamin fortification gave
margarine nutritional equivalency with butter. It took on a
new emphasis about 1958 when margarines appeared to meet
the views of some doctors that polyunsaturated fatty acids
were helpful in the dietary treatment of heart disease.

Flavor is, understandably, a significant theme which receives
restatement as flavoring techniques improve. In 1969 many
margarines referred to their "buttery" flavor in distinction from
former comparisons to "the more expensive spread." Laws
forbid dairy terminology that would cause consumers to think
that the product was butter, but most such laws do not appear
to bar explanations of product characteristics.

In the same display case with the advertised brands are often found the store brands. All of the national and many of the large regional food chains maintain their own brands and these retailers have their margarines made by manufacturers who specialize in this production. The larger chains require their margarines to meet their own specifications. Voluntary retail organizations frequently have their own brands also.

One purpose of these lower-priced products is to enable the store to participate profitably in the margarine market and to encourage traffic. Store brand margarines cost less because promotion is minimal or non-existent. These margarines undoubtedly increase total consumption.

Store label margarines also serve the function of presenting consumers with a price alternative backed by good basic quality. Close to half of all margarine purchased is of this class. It is non-innovative and tends to minimize the manufacturer's investment in plant and production.

All margarines, however, have their utility. There is room for all.[5]

Margarine's record on average retail prices has been mentioned. All things considered, it seems fair to say that this food has been a good purchase for consumers generally, evaluating its nutritional and other product values, its prices, and the cost of its major alternate, butter. Manufacturers have had the advantage of ample ingredient supplies, usually at acceptable prices. They have also absorbed much of the increased costs of labor, equipment and investment by increasing production efficiency and in narrow profit margins.

This is not the place for a technical discussion of margarine costs and prices. The special relationship between margarine and butter has long intrigued experts who study the effects of margarine, as a substitute purchase factor, on consumers' choices.[6] There is no doubt that increases in the cost of producing butter and the government price support floor for that product have helped margarine consumption.

Fundamentally the margarine price in the store is the result of a competitive process that affects all brands and product categories—this is reflected in the variations of margarine retail prices between brands, areas, stores, different sales days, and so forth. When special taxes have been removed, as by the federal tax repeal act of 1950 and the Idaho law of 1967, retail prices have immediately dropped by the amount of the tax.

One student of marketing notes the pride the American housewife takes in her shopping ability. "She is willing to pay high prices when convinced that she is obtaining comparable value, but she is likely to resist buying butter when margarine can be obtained for a fraction of the cost. Once accustomed to buying margarine, she may well be receptive to better and more expensive products—at least for certain uses."[7]

In the Store

Total food store sales of margarine, as mentioned previously, amount to over 1800 million pounds. The dollar sales volume may be estimated at approximately half a billion dollars. One study compares margarine and butter dollar sales for an earlier year.[8]

Of the products merchandised by food stores, margarine now ranks about twenty-fifth in dollar sales gains.[9] Chains handle about 60 per cent. The rest is divided between voluntary affiliated stores and small outlets such as the corner grocery and delicatessen. Practically all food stores now carry the spread—a far cry from its poor representation before World War II. Larger stores may carry as many as half a dozen brands; large supermarkets often offer a dozen or more.

Margarine has been credited with holding an average of 10 to 12 per cent of the display space, accounting for five per cent of dollar sales. Although it does not come near the really big items—meats and baked foods—in dollar sales, it is a growth item that suits the distribution techniques in which the modern supermarkets specialize.

The store's allocation and use of the best display place—the refrigerated case—is important to sales. Refrigerated space is costly; the struggle for position in it is unceasing. A store may discard a brand that is not earning its way although thereby it may disappoint some of its customers. Or it may give prime space to its own brand. In general margarine is reported to show a good return on per dollar of store investment and to be high in sales volume and profitability to the retailer.[10]

1. The monthly report of margarine production is in U.S. Bureau of the Census report, M20K. The package report is prepared for the National Association of Margarine Manufacturers.

2. Courtesy of A. C. Nielsen Company and trade sources.

3. F. H. Graf, *Logistics of Grocery Products* (Chicago, A. C. Nielsen Company, 1968), 9.

4. See National Commission on Food Marketing, *Studies of Organization and Competition in Grocery Manufacturing* (Washington, 1966), 30-39.

5. *Food Topics*, XXIII, 30, 38 (September, 1968). *Grocery Manufacturer*, II, 14 (July, 1968) reports margarine dollar sales in chain stores for January-March 1968 to be $9,221,000 nearly 12 per cent more than for the comparable 1967 period.

6. Examples are W. R. Pabst, *Butter and Margarine* (New York, 1937); A. S. Rojko, *Demand and Price Structure for Dairy Products* (Washington, 1957); and D. Feinberg, "A Case Study in Substitution: Butter and Margarine" (ms. dissertation, New York University, 1961). In view of its leadership in the spread field it is debatable whether the traditional approach to margarine economics as those of simple substitution only is any longer valid. Other factors would seem to have significance, especially since the introduction of premium margarines.

7. R. D. Tousley, "Margarine Marketing," ms.; I am indebted to Unilever, N. V. for permission to use Dr. Tousley's paper. His comprehensive chapter on the subject is in the *Margarine Centenary Book* ('S-Gravenhage, 1969).

8. R. D. Buzzell and R. E. Nourse, *Product Innovations in Food Processing, 1954-64* (Boston, 1967), 55-58.

9. *Food Topics*, XXIII, 19 (September 1968).

10. *Supermarket News*, April 15, 1968, 24.

V

The Nutritional Role

Fats are important to good nutrition—more so than many weight-conscious Americans are aware. We eat a variety of foods with significant fat content, not always recognizing the amount of fat in those foods or its nutritional significance. Margarine is one of the food fats. Its primary nutritional contribution is food energy or calories. It also provides certain related food values.

Nutrition is a younger science. Its major developments have taken place within the last hundred years. They have dramatically changed our knowledge of food and health. Real progress has been within the last half century, paralleling the emergence of margarine.

The historic findings of science concerning food energy, vitamins, fatty acids, and the significance of food fats to body health and processes have all had effect on the composition of modern margarine. The inventor of the first "oleomargarine" considered his product to be a definite help to better human nutrition and against hunger. Indeed it was.

Much fuller information has become available since World War II concerning fats as well as proteins and other nutrients, and a good deal of scientific research is underway in fats nutrition. This has drawn attention to margarine. The probability is that new findings will cause knowledge of the dietary requirements for fats to be much more sophisticated and will better document their value in our food system.

Margarine's basic nutritional contributions are as follows:

(1) Food energy, which it provides at the level of about 3,300 calories per pound.

(2) Vitamin A, which it provides at a minimum level of 15,000 U.S.P. units per pound.

"Wasn't That Kind of Cow"
(Warren in the Cincinnati Inquirer)

(3) Essential and polyunsaturated fatty acids. (The principal one is linoleic acid.)

Also present are minor nutrients which vary somewhat between margarines: vitamin D (by fortification), vitamin E (naturally present in vegetable oils, in variable amounts), and fractional amounts of proteins and minerals.

Margarine, like most foods, is just one source of the nutrients it contains. It contributes to a good diet; it is not a nutritional end in itself. Margarine's assignment is twofold—to help satisfy hunger quickly and to furnish savor and palatability. It helps us enjoy foods that otherwise would be distinctly less palatable.

All food fats create richness, savor and the finer enjoyment of eating. Margarine does this in a special way. It is a fatty food, not just a fat. There are margarines high in polyunsaturated fatty acids; margarines that are all vegetable, or blends of vegetable and animal fats; and low-salt and kosher or parve margarines as described in the opening chapter.

EQUIVALENCY

Nutritional science began with the concept that fats were useful simply to supply body energy. For a long time fats were regarded as uncomplicated, compact energy sources. Health authorities early bestowed their approval on the first oleomargarines, identifying them as nutritional equivalents of butter.

Scientists later sought to isolate vitamins and define their vital function. The fat-soluble vitamins were identified after 1912; vitamin A was found to exist, though variably, in butter; vitamin D was believed to be present in butterfat in a smaller amount. For a time oleomargarines were given lesser status because they lacked significant amounts of vitamin A.

The introduction of vitamin fortification gave margarine a new nutritional respectability, for fortified margarines could offer the A in reliable, uniform quantity. At first the level was "standardized" to provide a minimum of 9,000 U.S.P. units per pound, to comply with the then estimated average for butter. When that estimate was lifted to 15,000 units, margarine's minimum amount of vitamin A was put at that level. Many margarines also were fortified with vitamin D, usually to provide a minimum of 2,000 U.S.P. units a pound, and this continues in some brands.

By 1940 the nutritional equivalency of the two "spreads" had been re-established as far as nutritional knowledge then went. The consumer who bought margarines was getting the same nutrients but at lower cost. The federal Agriculture and Labor Departments began to recommend fortified margarines in 1939.

By then fortification and a general improvement of the spread had won it favorable attention among physicians, dietitians, nutritionists and home economists. Favorable scientific testimony accumulated. The Food, Drug, and Cosmetic Act of 1938 set up a procedure for standardizing foods in terms of compositional requirements and involving nutritional criteria. Soon there appeared the "Definition and Standard of Identity for Oleomargarine." It fixed the fat and the food energy component at 80 per cent—the same as in butter. It also permitted fortification with vitamins A or D.[1]

The government had set a floor under the best nutritional standards for margarine then known. The concept of food value equivalency between margarine and butter was approved. By providing for a fairly wide choice of ingredients and for possible new ingredients by future changes, the Standard kept open an important door to nutritional improvements of margarine. Margarine was no longer a butter substitute. Claims by dairy interests against it as an inferior food began to disappear. The removal of legal restrictions on margarine's sale began.

World War II caused nutrition to be emphasized as a matter of public policy, while fat shortages directed renewed attention to margarine as a low-cost food of dietary significance. The equivalency idea received significant restatement by medical and scientific organizations, commencing in 1942 with a key declaration by the Council on Foods and Nutrition of the American Medical Association. New research gave confirmation.

"Margarine," said Dr. Anton J. Carlson in 1942, "can now be produced having the digestibility, nutritive value, flavor, and keeping qualities of our best summer butter, including vitamins A and D."[1]

The National Research Council highlighted these events in a special report on margarine in 1943 which concluded that, fortified with vitamin A, "no nutritional difference" from butter could be observed when used in a mixed diet. A year later the American Medical Association advised wartime America that fortified margarine could be "substituted in the ordinary diet without any nutritional disadvantage."[3] Margarine appeared as part of the then basic seven food groups. When the issue of removing the old federal taxes on margarine arose in Congress, scientists gave effective nutritional testimony.

In 1951 the Standard was amended to increase the minimum of vitamin A fortification. There have been various changes since, involving coloring, flavorings, and ingredients. These amendments, some more important than others, helped enlarge the distinction between margarine and butter. Margarine began to leave strict equivalency with the other spread behind and to be seen as embodying differences, chiefly in reliability of vitamin A content and in polyunsaturated fatty acid content.

As Food Fat

Margarine is one of the large family of substances called fats (oil is the customary name when the fat is liquid at room temperature). To some fat is a word associated with overindulgence. But it also means richness and savor, and it has become much more valued as a dietary factor than it used to be. "A fat-free diet is, without qualification, inedible for any length of time," it has been observed.[4]

Food fat as a contributor of nutrition rates as one of the basic trio—protein, carbohydrates, and fat. Each of these classes has won its own nutritional significance. Each is life-giving. Americans choose from a lavish array and are fortunate they can do so. Margarine is a food fat notable for being consumed in increasing volume.

The body can get energy quickly, efficiently and cheaply from fat; it is concentrated food energy. Fat supplies more than twice the calories in metabolism (9 per gram) as the same amount of protein (4 per gram) or the same amount of carbohydrate (4 per gram). The body utilizes it efficiently and requires it in reasonable amounts to stop hunger, to store energy, to protect vital organs, and to create a sense of well-being.

The fat in margarine as in any other food performs these nutritional tasks. It helps the body utilize proteins, carbohydrates, the fat-soluble vitamins, and minerals. It contributes vitamin A and, in small amounts, other fat-soluble vitamins and a vitamin-like substance known as choline. It provides fatty acids. It is 99 per cent digestible.

As a food fat margarine is fairly unique. The fat content of many foods varies, as in meat or rich baked foods. Margarine's is constant, like that of lard and shortening, but those foods are 100 per cent fat (or nearly so), while margarine is 80 per cent fat. In this respect it is like butter, but while the latter is always one animal fat—milkfat—margarine may be a combination of oils or fats.

MARGARINE AND CALORIES

Since providing calories—food energy—is the main business of food fats, margarine is related to the subject of calories in the food we eat. A calorie is, of course, the established and convenient way of expressing a unit of food energy. Regular margarine supplies about 200 calories per ounce, the equivalents being about 100 calories per tablespoon and about 7.4 calories per gram.

Whipped margarines have the same calories per pound or ounce. Because of the greater volume of product per pound, their calorie provision per pat or teaspoonful is a third less. Lower-fat margarines ordinarily have about half as many calories per unit of volume as the regular margarines.

Calorie-conscious Americans have become well acquainted with the fact that one obtains food energy not just from the obvious visible sources such as the pat of margarine on the plate or the dressing on the salad but from a large number of foods. Diet books frequently point out that a good gravy or ice cream or meat dish will supply a high level of calories. For that matter so will a martini, or a candy bar, or many other foods or beverages.

Eaten in usual amounts as part of regular meals, margarine will account for only a small part of the daily caloric intake of most persons. To omit the fats visible on one's plate will not necessarily bring about any radical change in one's calorie consumption. It may indeed be nutritionally unwise. Choosing the right food is all a matter of balance, like most things having to do with our health.

We really do not know exactly the total number of calories from all sources that the average American consumes. Two helpful guides may be mentioned. One, a report on the amount of calories consumed, based on a 1965 government survey of consumption levels, found that fats contributed about 41 per cent of the calories in the nation's available food supply. A supplementary report discovered less food energy in various diets than in the recommended dietary allowances but could draw no conclusions as to additional calorie needs. A statement issued by the federal government and dealing with sources of calories indicates that about 39 per cent of the fat sources are the familiar visibles, margarine, shortening, lard, butter and others, whether as separate foods or as hidden ingredients. The rest is unseen fat in milk, cheese, meat and many other foods.[5]

Recent scentific inquiry involving overweight and related diseases has directed new attention to the American diet makeup. One report, prepared some years ago for the use of physicians and professional students of the problem, indicated the total disappearance of fats into the national food supply to be 145 grams per person per day. That would be five ounces, or 1,300 calories. Actually, consumption—what is actually eaten—may be closer to about 4 ounces or 1,080 calories.

Interestingly, despite the increase in vegetable fats in our diet this total reflected 66 per cent of food and fat from animal sources. The other 34 per cent was vegetable fat. Margarine's total disappearance into the food supply amounted to 10.1 grams a day, the equivalent of less than half an ounce, or 94 calories. Most of this was vegetable oil or fat.[6] The margarine contribution today would be higher absolutely and in terms of vegetable fat.

Americans have been reducing their consumption of the starchy carbohydrates, especially potatoes and cereals. Meanwhile the consumption of food fats has increased. The familiar visible fats have kept a remarkable level rate of consumption —around 51.8 pounds per person per year. Of this, in 1969, all margarine provided about 8.6 pounds (the fat content). The following figures are illustrative for earlier years:

SOURCES OF NUTRIENT FAT IN THE DIET FROM THE "VISIBLE" FATS
(Grams, Per Capita)

	Vegetable Fats			Animal Fats	
Year	Margarine	All	Butter	Margarine	All
1947-49	5.5	25.2	10.6	0.1	27.5
1957-59	8.7	31.9	8.2	0.2	24.5
1965	9.5	38.7	6.5	0.6	20.8

Source: *American Journal of Clinical Nutrition*, 20:911 (August 1967).

Margarine consumption is not nutritionally excessive overall. In comparison with other countries where it is used, its consumption in the United States is low and probably smaller than it could be within a well-balanced diet, compared with other calorie-important foods. The spread is important in the American fat input but it is not the major factor in the calories derived from well-supplied American diets. As a calorie provider it is useful, it is variable between individuals, it is related to the consumption of basic foods, and it is supplementary.

Every weight-conscious person understandably is more interested in his personal question than in averages. "How much fat should I eat?" A general recommendation is issued from time to time by the National Research Council. Its latest report, in 1968, took a fresh and wide look at the American dietary scene. The report suggested reduced caloric requirements for different classes or groups.

The food energy expenditures it reported for its reference examples—men weighing 70 kilograms (154 pounds) and 22 years of age, and women weighing 58 kilograms (128 pounds) and and the same age—came to 2,810 and 2,050 calories per day respectively. These calculations entail certain assumptions.

The recommended caloric allowance for men varies according to their weight, from 2,200 calories for men of 110 pounds weight to 3,700 for men of twice that weight. For women, the range is given from 1,550 calories (88 pounds) to 2,300 (154 pounds). Adjustments are made in the allowances recommended for younger persons and lactating women.[7] One comment in 1964 seems as much in order now as then: "The proper caloric allowance for an individual is that which will maintain body weight and health and at a level most conducive to to his well-being."[8]

Abundant medical and nutritional evidence points to the conclusion that Americans by and large are getting enough food energy, always excepting hunger and malnutrition in some groups. A frequent recommendation is that approximately 25-35 per cent of one's calories should be in the form of fat. This level (which some might find modest) fits into present-day scientific thinking. Diets should be "varied, adequate, and not overly rich" with "judicious control of caloric intake and daily exercise," as one authority expresses it.[9]

To sum up, margarine's calories do the job all calories do. They are neither "stronger" nor "weaker," "good" nor "bad."

It is the kind of fat, rather than the calories, that invites study and discussion.

The Make-up of Food Fat

It has been observed earlier in this book that the fat portion of most of the margarines consumed today in the United States is a blend of vegetable oils. These oils constituted 93 per cent of all the fats in margarine in 1969, the principal one being soybean oil. Margarines are composed of vegetable fat or of vegetable and animal fat. Vegetable oils and animal fats and their blends are equally nutritious with respect to food energy, digestibility, and general healthfulness.

Nutritionists have noted the shift in the American food supply over the last half a century from food fats that are animal fats (lard, butter, and some shortenings) to those that are predominantly or all vegetable oils (most margarines and shortenings, salad oils and dressings and mayonnaise, for example). Americans have been exchanging food fats. This shift has not occasioned any noticeable nutritional loss. Its general effect in fact has been limited.

Nevertheless the change has brought into the American diet a different content of fatty acids. Margarine has been one of the significant factors.

The development of better research techniques has enabled more attention to be given to the chemical nature of fats and how food fat is absorbed and utilized by the body. This nutritional pioneering has enlisted large resources. It has also inspired floods of newspaper and popular magazine comment, some conflicting, much not conclusive scientifically, and much confusing to the ordinary consumer. A glance at the basic chemistry involved helps one understand margarine's relationship to these important nutritional events.

Fats are chemical combinations as are all things. As such, they are "built" of fatty acids and glycerol. Some 95 per cent of fat is, in effect, fatty acids. Each edible oil or fat possesses its own typical combinations of these substances.

The fatty acids in turn are composed of combinations of carbon, hydrogen, and oxygen atoms. The basic arrangement of such a molecule is diagrammed by chemists as a chain of carbon atoms. The length of the carbon atom chain and the degree to which it is "saturated" is what makes a fat what it is and distinguishes one kind of fat from another. Each of the carbon atoms in the chain can connect or link with two hydrogen atoms in addition to two other carbon atoms.

If all the carbon atoms are so linked, the fat is known as "saturated" because the carbon atoms have all of the potential linkage saturated with hydrogen or carbon atoms. When two adjoining carbon atoms in a single chain are both missing one hydrogen atom, the fatty acid is "monounsaturated." When more than one set of carbon atoms in a single chain are missing one hydrogen atom each, the fat is "polyunsaturated."

A broad difference exists among food fats as to their physical and chemical characteristics. In general, fats that are poly-unsaturated to a fairly significant extent—that is, that contain a fairly significant amount of unsaturated fatty acids—originate in soybean, corn, cottonseed, safflower or other vegetable oil-seeds. Unsaturated fats tend to be liquid at room temperature. Animal fats (and coconut oil) are more on the saturated side. They are mostly solid at room temperature and are sometimes known as hard fats, like that on a good steak.

But here, too, over-simplification can be misleading. No food fat is all polyunsaturated or saturated.

The fatty acids in fats and oils are linked together in systems called triglycerides. These are combinations of three fatty acid molecules attached to one glycerine molecule and may be depicted in this manner:

$$\text{Glycerine} \begin{cases} \text{Fatty acid (stearic acid, saturated)} \\ \text{Fatty acid (oleic acid, monounsaturated)} \\ \text{Fatty acid (linoleic acid, polyunsaturated)} \end{cases}$$

Chemists have found that the fatty acids themselves determine the physical properties of the fats we eat. Nutritionists have sought to ascertain the nutritional properties of the different fatty acids.

ESSENTIAL FATTY ACIDS

About a generation ago linoleic and arachidonic fatty acids were defined as "essential" because they were thought to be vital to body growth, reproduction, and skin health. Linoleic acid is the most important nutritionally because it is more abundant in foods and cannot be produced within the body, but must be secured by means of the food we eat. "There can be little doubt that these substances are required nutrients for man," according to the American Medical Association.[10] Their requirement level in the diet however, is not high.[11]

Both of these fatty acids occur in margarines. Linoleic acid is a significant nutrient in most margarines, owing to its considerable presence in the vegetable oils frequently used in margarines. How the margarine is formulated and processed, of course, will influence the amount of linoleic acid it supplies. A "regular," average-priced margarine may contain around 10 to 15 per cent of this essential fatty acid. Many "special" margarines are designed to provide as much as 30 to 40 per cent, some as high as 60 per cent. In all cases the presence of linoleic acid in margarines, relative to that in most other foods, is high.[12]

The essential fatty acids are not limited to vegetable oils. They are present also in animal fats, although in these the linoleic acid content is lower than that of the vegetable oils.

Fatty Acids and Heart Disease

The distinction between polyunsaturated and saturated fatty acids has been given new nutritional emphasis within the last twenty years by those who believe that diet bears some relationship to heart disease and related health problems, and that, in particular, the evidence would indicate that the substitution of polyunsaturated fatty acids for some of the more saturated fatty acids might be helpful in lowering the incidence of heart and vascular diseases.

This belief has been based on findings that a person consuming a diet high in saturated fatty acid content is likely to have a higher level of a substance called "cholesterol" in his blood. Cholesterol is a normal component of the blood. But it has been found as a deposit on the inner walls of blood vessels. There it can obstruct the passage of blood and presumably contribute in

some manner not yet entirely known to the accident commonly known as a heart attack.[13]

A great deal of publicity has been given the concept that fats
high in polyunsaturated fatty acids, such as linoleic acid, can
be helpful in the treatment of heart disease. Here we confront a
complicated and highly technical subject. The evidence is by no
means all in hand to prove the actual relationship between
cholesterol in the blood and heart or circulatory disorders. The
discussion continues at the scientific level where much research is going forward. Among other fruits of that research, it
has been established that cholesterol itself performs necessary
metabolic functions and the body manufactures more of it
than one ordinarily gets from one's food.

Margarine has been spotlighted in this important but un-
finished debate. It is a good source of polyunsaturates and therefore has been given a place in the diet suggestions by those who
consider a lower intake of saturated fats to be desirable. Margarine can be formulated to increase its content of polyunsaturated fatty acids, principally linoleic. Special margarines
have been developed for this purpose, relying on formulas or
oils high in polyunsaturates.

Brands of margarine vary in their fatty acid composition
according to the oils they contain and their method of manufacture. Each of the fats and oils is named in the order of predominance on the main panel of the package. The American
Medical Association a few years ago distinguished between
"regular" and "special" margarines. The latter it classed as those
with higher polyunsaturate values, rating them as a group to
contain about 22 to 54 per cent polyunsaturates (grams of fatty
acid, as glyceride ester, per 100 grams of margarine). "Regular"
margarines it rated at 7 to 15 per cent.[14]

More recently this classification has been applied by another
report which applies to vegetable margarines and which may be
presented as shown by the table on the next page.

Polyunsaturates	Regular Margarines	Special Margarines
Dienoic (chiefly linoleic)	10-20	22- 60
Trienoic (chiefly linolenic)	0- 0.5	0- 0.5
Monounsaturates (chiefly monoenoic, or oleic)	42-63	20- 57
Saturates	16-25	13- 30
Iodine Value	78-90	92-130

Source: Institute of Shortening and Edible Oils, *Food Fats and Oils* (Washington, 1968), 16.

By way of comparison there are reported from the same study the fatty acid compositions for certain other familiar food fats:

Polyunsaturates	Butterfat	Household Vegetable Shortening Regular	Household Vegetable Shortening Special	Lard*
Dienoic (chiefly linoleic)	1.0- 2.5	6-14	22-23	7-13
Trienoic (chiefly linolenic)	0.2- 0.5	0- 1.0	0- 2.5	0.1
Monounsaturates (chiefly monoenoic, or oleic)	28-31	53-75	44-55	44-53
Saturates	63-70	19-33	22-32	34-45
Iodine Value	30-40	70-81	85-95	63-69

*Reported as all meat fat household shortening.
Source: Institute of Edible Oils and Shortening, *Food Fats and Oils* (Washington, 1968), 15, 16.

The composition of the total supply of fatty acids available to each person in the United States in 1965 has been figured to have been 19 grams polyunsaturated, 59 grams monounsaturated, and 54 grams saturated.

It should be observed that recommendations of scientific organizations have differed on the subject of polyunsaturates and heart disease. One has advised doctors and laymen alike to reduce the amount of fat in the diet and even to limit fat use somewhat within the bounds of a well-balanced diet. It also suggests a substitution of food fats higher in polyunsaturates (such as margarine) for those higher in saturates.[15]

Other authoritative professional organizations, while not contradicting this position directly, have urged consumers not to undertake radical self-prescribed diet changes. They caution against excessive fat dieting.[16] Under these circumstances the average person would seem best advised to go by his doctor's counsel.

A related subject is that of hydrogenation, the process whereby the melting point of a liquid oil or fat is sufficiently raised to yield a fat that is plastic at room temperature.[17] A melting range is secured that will cause the spread to "break" in the mouth pleasingly and quickly, a necessity for good palatability. Virtually all plastic margarine melts at between 90° and 97° F. (32° to 36° C.) or slightly below normal body temperature.

Hydrogenation is a controlled chemical process that partly arranges fat molecules so that some hydrogen atoms are added to the oil. It is extremely useful in food processing. It minimizes susceptibility of the treated oil to oxidation and rancidity.

Products for consumer use are never completely hydrogenated. The application of the process to the oils in margarine is limited. In many margarines with more than one oil, only one may be partially hydrogenated; the other or others may remain liquid. Or all the fat components may be slightly hydrogenated. Thus, while the process transforms some of the polyunsaturated fatty acid chains into saturates, other are unchanged. Some of the linoleic acid present in the original fat or oil remains in the finished product. The monounsaturate content is increased more than the saturate content.

Incompletely hydrogenated liquid oil can comprise up to 75 per cent of the entire fat portion of the margarine formulation. Soft margarines require little hydrogenation. Liquid margarine is composed of very lightly hydrogenated oils.

It is apparent that much is yet to be learned about the precise role of fatty acids in nutrition. Meanwhile the amount of polyunsaturates the American consumer is eating appears to have increased substantially. The supermarket, someone has calculated, now "sells" an estimated 31 per cent more polyunsaturates (in the form of many different foods) than forty years ago. Margarine has figured in this development also.

Vitamin A Standardization

The vitamin A fortification minimum of 15,000 U.S.P. units means that a ½ ounce pat provides 470 units. Most of the A in margarine is man-made. It may be combined with carotene — a yellow precursor substance that the body converts to vitamin A and that also is one of the yellow coloring materials for the margarine. Some natural vitamin A is used.

Vitamin A, the "yellow vitamin," is associated with various green and yellow foods because of their carotene content. Its specific contributions to health are good vision, healthy skin, strong teeth and general well-being. Not long ago the recommended daily amounts of vitamin A for good health were readjusted by the National Research Council. For adults the recommendation is now 5,000 U.S.P. units per day, while for all ages and conditions the range is from 1,500 to 8,000 units.[18] A food consumption survey made in 1965 disclosed that some American diets today may not contain those recommended levels of the vitamin[19]—a subject that nutritionists continue to review.

Margarine kept in 41° F storage for a little more than a year has been found to retain an average of 83 per cent of the different vitamin A substances with which the product had been fortified. A reasonably varied diet including margarine usually makes unnecessary the trouble and cost of special vitamin supplements.

The standardization of vitamin A content created a uniformity of this nutritional factor that had not been the case with table spread before. It is the basis of the dietary statement that is labeled on the package and which most commonly states that "2 ounces supply 47 per cent of vitamin A minimum daily requirement" or something similar.

Minor Nutrients

Besides food energy, fatty acids, and vitamin A, margarine contains minor nutrients. These may be described briefly.

Vitamin D, the "sunlight" or anti-rickets factor, is not a major factor in most margarines though it may be added through fortification, ordinarily at the rate of 2,000 U.S.P. units per pound. This practice is decreasing, though some margarines continue to provide this amount of the vitamin.

Vitamin E, or alpha tocopherol, is now much more than formerly regarded as nutritionally important. Among other properties, it inhibits the oxidation of the vegetable oils in which it naturally occurs, especially those that are polyunsaturated. Attention has been attracted to the ability of this vitamin to assist the body's utilization of polyunsaturates by slowing down their tendency to oxidize during metabolism. Most vegetable oil margarines contain vitamin E, but it varies in amount according to the oils used.

Vitamin K is present in vegetable oil margarines because of its existence in their constituent oils. Its amount is very small.

Skim milk (or nonfat dry milk reconstituted with water) is, in terms of volume, the largest single component of most margarines other than the fat. It is being incorporated to the extent of about 17 to 18 per cent of the weight of the product. The milk solids content is about 1.5 per cent of the product weight; the nutrient contribution is minor.

Soy milk, composed of a protein fraction extracted from ground soybeans, is incorporated in certain margarines in lieu of dairy milk in order to make available a product devoid of animal-origin ingredients.

Salt usually takes up to 1½ to 3 per cent of the product weight. Certain margarines are available without salt. They are sometimes referred to as low sodium margarines.

Emulsifiers that may be present in margarine and are most widely used are lecithin, a natural component of soybean and certain other oils; monoglycerides and diglycerides; and—used to a lesser degree—tartaric acid esters of mono- and diglycerides. These are used in amounts less than 0.5 per cent of the product weight. They do not significantly affect the nutrient content although they provide small amounts of food energy qualities.

These and all other ingredients of margarine are declared on

the label. If the margarine is sold expressly for dietary purposes (low-fat, all-vegetable, kosher), the label will bear a statement to that effect.

1. The Standard for regular margarine, setting forth the permitted ingredients and other composition requirements, will be found in the Code of Federal
Regulations, the reference being 21 C.F.R. 45.1. A Standard for liquid margarine is only slightly different (21 C.F.R. 45.2). That for margarine containing animal fat is in 9 C.F.R. 328.1.

2. "Address on Margarine," April 30, 1942 (mimeographed); also American
Medical Association, *Journal*, 119:1455-7 (August 22, 1942); A. J. Carlson,
M.D., comp., *Legislation Which Renders It More Difficult To Secure Ade-
quate Nutrition* (Chicago, 1943).

3. National Research Council, *A Report on Margarine* (Washington, 1943),
18; American Medical Association, *Journal*, 126:168 (September 16, 1944).

4. National Research Council, *Symposium on Atherosclerosis* (Washington,
1954), 172. See also its *Dietary Fat and Human Health* (Washington, 1966),
21; and *Recommended Dietary Allowances* (Washington, 1968), 10-13.

5. B. Friend, "Nutrients in United States Food Supply," in *American
Journal of Clinical Nutrition*, 20:909 (August, 1967); U. S. Department of
Agriculture, *Food Intake and Nutritive Value of Diets in the United States,
Spring 1965* (Washington, 1969), 10; *id.*, "Civilian Consumption of Visible
Fats Per Person, 1949-62" (offset, n.p., n.d.).

6. American Medical Association, Council on Foods and Nutrition, "The
Regulation of Dietary Fat," in A.M.A. *Journal*, 181:421 (August 4, 1962).

7. National Research Council, *Recommended Dietary Allowances* (Washington, 1968), 1-9.

8. *Id., Recommended Dietary Allowances* (Washington, 1964), 10.

9. *Id., Dietary Fat and Human Health* (Washington, 1966), 43. See also the
National Research Council's *Recommended Dietary Allowances* (Washington,
1964), 30. The American Medical Association's Council on Foods and Nutrition
has found "little evidence that adjusting the fat content of the diet below or
above 40% of the calories will achieve better results in the management of
obesity" (A.M.A. *Journal*, 181:422, August 4, 1962).

10. American Medical Association, *Journal*, 181:421 (August 4, 1962). In
recent years a third fatty acid, linolenic, has been dropped from the "essential"
category.

11. National Research Council, *Recommended Dietary Allowances* (Washington, 1968), 12.

12. It is difficult to label the precise amount of one fatty acid or another in
margarine. One batch of a given oil may vary somewhat, though slightly, from
another. Too frequent restatements of labeling cannot be synchronized with
package printing except at a very considerable increase in cost and price.
Individual manufacturers can advise concerning their particular margarines.

The work often referred to for comparative nutritional contents of foods is the U. S. Department of Agriculture's "Handbook No. 8," entitled *Composition of Foods* (Washington, rev. ed., 1963). It reports the following information concerning margarine and butter. The subdivisions under "Margarine" represent the first ingredient named on the label.

Grams Per 100 Grams, Edible Portion	Margarine		Butter	Pages
	Hardened, Grams	Liquid, Grams	Grams	
Total Fat	81	81	81	132, 124
Total Saturated Fatty Acids	18	19	46	
Unsaturated Fatty Acids				
Oleic (monounsaturated)	47	31	27	
Linoleic (polyunsaturated)	14	29	2	

Cholesterol	Milligrams
Margarine:	Per Pound
All Vegetable Fat	0
2/3 Animal, 1/3 Vegetable	295
Butter	1,135

13. A recent description is Osmo Turpeinen, "Diet and Coronary Events," in American Dietetic Association, *Journal,* 52:209-13 (March, 1968).

14. American Medical Association, *Journal,* 171:719 (March 3, 1962).

15. American Heart Association, *Diet and Heart Disease* (New York, release of October 30, 1968), 2. See also the A.H.A. release of June 9, 1964.

16. American Medical Association, *Journal,* 194:247-8 (December 6, 1965); National Research Council, *Dietary Fat and Human Health* (Washington, 1966), 43; Nutrition Foundation, statement dated December 19, 1959 (mimeographed).

17. It is described more fully in Chapter III.

18. National Research Council, *Recommended Dietary Allowances* (Washington, 1968), 21-24 and table.

19. U. S. Department of Agriculture, *Dietary Levels of Households in the United States, Spring 1965* (Washington, 1968), Tables 5 and 6, See also *id., Food Intake and Nutritive Value of Diets . . . in the United States, Spring 1965* (Washington, 1969), 6.

VI

Margarine Law

No other food has a legal history quite like that pertaining to margarine. It has been the subject of countless legislative enactments and many court decisions. There are special provisions of federal law governing the product and there are special margarine laws in all but three states.

Special laws dealing with margarine came about when those wishing to protect butter from the competition of a new, butter-like spread sought government regulation. This effort went beyond regulation into outright restriction. The thrust was economic, not consumer protection.

Since the commencement of special margarine laws, regular federal and state laws have been established to protect the food buying public. They apply to foods of all kinds, including margarine. Their purpose is the modern one of regulating the purity of food products, their packaging and weight, their labeling and, to an extent, their manufacture. They are consumer laws. They exist side by side with the special margarine laws and cover the same ground in most important respects.

Not surprisingly, legislation to restrict the sale of margarine was controversial. The special laws enacted to curtail its availability were brought before the courts on many occasions. Some have historic significance beyond the immediate margarine question that was involved. To describe these ramifications is beyond the scope of this description of margarine law. The landmark cases are described later in this chapter.

The margarine legal history is unique. It continues to influence the way the product is sold in some states. The long record of the movement to suppress margarine, which came to a virtual end during the nineteen-fifties, is inevitably in the minds of many of the legislators who are called upon to pass control measures

regulating the various new foods such as mellorine and filled
and non-dairy milk. Such legislation reflects conflicts between
producer and consumer protection similar, though not as harsh,
to that which attended the development of margarine.

This description of margarine law is necessarily a summary.
It does, however, comprehend the principal aspects and will
serve as a guide to the legal student. Full citations to the statutes,
regulations and court decisions referred to are appended. The
next chapter reviews the history of margarine, legislative events
being a prominent part of the story.

THE SPECIAL LAWS

The major means of restriction that came to receive acceptance by Congress and the Supreme Court were the prohibition
of colored margarine, the artificial increase of price by margarine
taxation, and certain barriers to distribution or consumption by
means of licensing, denial of government purchasing, special
handling of packaging requirements, etc.

By 1969 such coercive provisions, once dominant, had been
mostly removed by legislatures or, in a few instances, by court
actions.[1] What is left of special margarine law is chiefly, though
not entirely, regulative. The remaining regulatory parts of the
old margarine laws are by and large a superimposed patchwork
on existing food regulatory law. Their removal would simplify
pure food regulation.

Certain characteristics of their legal treatment of margarine
are worth noting for they throw light on earlier concepts of
dealing with food substitution or with the regulation of foods
introduced by invention and science. They also involve a federal
commerce clause. In this connection it may be noted that re-
pressive laws for margarine were not peculiar to the United
States although the American laws generally inclined to be
much more harshly restrictive than those developed in Western
Europe. The frank intent was to establish an internal protectionist system against margarine in favor of dairy butter. The
Constitution's mantle of protection of interstate commerce may

Embattled dairy farmers find
medieval walls are no defense

"If he's no good, what are you afraid of?"
(Lewis in the Milwaukee Journal)

have helped significantly to save oleomargarine from flat suppression in many states if not federally.

One characteristic of these laws that still abides is the application of criminal penalties for infractions. This is true of the Federal and many state pure food laws, but under the older "oleomargarine" statutes, the food was thrust into the legal company of, for example, harmful drugs. It was permitted to be taxed on the ground of being an object of possible public injury, like tobacco or liquor. Further, its availability to consumers was hindered by trade barriers, the only major food so jeopardized.[2]

Another feature was the legal distinction established in state law (after 1886) and federal law (in 1902) between uncolored margarine and colored margarine (or oleomargarine). The latter fell under higher taxes than the former and, in many states, outright prohibition. This legal differentiation still remains.

Yet another aspect was the statutory definition of the product name "oleomargarine" (and, more recently, "margarine") and statement of its ingredients and composition. The original aim was economic—not so much to bestow on the food a clear identity of its own but to distinguish it from dairy butter. As one result, oleomargarine or margarine is often defined by statute in close congruity with other products that are different; for instance, adulterated or renovated butter.

Terminology persists that creates problems as new products enter the field. Thus, in some states margarine is "imitation butter" or "butter substitute" while in others it is not. The establishment of the federal definition of the product in 1941 and its periodic amendment since have not entirely dispelled this cloudy legal nomenclature.

There is a frequent and difficult lack of uniformity. While in practice a general uniformity in labeling and package weights has been achieved under the Federal Margarine Act of 1950, there remain all sorts of deviations in the old state laws. In practical effect these now show up in only a few labeling curiosities, but the necessity exists for a designer of a margarine label to consider a large number of federal and state laws. The National Association of Margarine Manufacturers has compiled a guide to labeling and other requirements to help marketers find their way through this legal jungle. Even so, requirements are much more uniform than they have been for many years, owing to legislative changes.

More interesting is the area in which federal margarine law seeks to preempt state powers over intrastate commerce. The justification given in the Act of 1950 is that colored margarine's sale constitutes a substantial effect on national commerce in dairy butter. That law extends the regulative powers of the national pure food regulative agency, the United States Food and Drug Administration, into public eating places serving colored margarine, regardless of the product's origin in commerce, and indeed over the sale of colored margarine generally, although state laws are preserved. The restaurant provision has been criticized as needlessly detailed, strict, and difficult to enforce. The Act grants special powers to the Federal Trade Commission over margarine advertising, and a question exists concerning this authorization also.

Students may find these instances some precedent for the wide federal powers in state regulative work granted in the Fair Labeling and Packaging Act of 1966 and the Wholesome Meat Act of 1967. At any event, the most sophisticated reconciler of inter- and intrastate laws may well conclude that the existing margarine legal structure is excessively complicated and overlapping. The eventual solution in the interest of simple uniformity (which would tend toward lower costs to consumers) may not altogether succumb to federal precedent and rulemaking. One proposal is to let the model state pure food law take over entirely from the state margarine statutes.

Principal Laws and Federal Regulations

A comprehensive collection of the different legal requirements is an essential adjunct to the marketing of margarine to consumers. The authoritative one is the *Compilation of Federal and State Laws on Margarine* maintained by the National Association of Margarine Manufacturers for its members.

Adapting from the "Compilation," but broadening the list to include other applicable food statutes, the following is an outline of the major federal laws:

Federal Margarine Act 1950.

Federal Food, Drug, and Cosmetic Act of 1938, as amended with particular reference to the Margarine Act of 1950 amendments, the Color Additives Amendment of 1960 and the Food Additives Amendment of 1958.

Wholesome Meat Act of 1967.

Federal Trade Commission Act of 1914, as amended, with particular reference to the Margarine Act of 1950 amendments.

Section I of the Navy Ration Statue of 1933, as amended.

Fair Packaging and Labeling Act of 1966.

The major federal regulations under the above are as follows:

Food and Drug Administration: (1) Definition and Standard of Identity for Margarine, Oleomargarine; (2) the same for liquid margarine, oleomargarine; (3) Interpretative Regulations Respecting the labeling of Oleomargarine or Margarine (1950); (4) Food Labeling Regulations under the Fair Packaging and Labeling Act of 1966 (1967); (5) "Declaration of Policy" concerning the labeling of foods containing polyunsaturated fatty acids (1959).

U. S. Department of Agriculture's Definition and Standard of Identity for Margarine, Oleomargarine, incorporating animal fat (other than milk fat); and other regulations concerning meat products applicable to such margarine inspection.

These are the various types of applicable state laws:

Special Margarine Laws. The oldest is believed to date back to 1878.

Pure Food Laws. Some 33 are in the form of the model state pure food law prepared by the Association of Food and Drug Officials of the United States.

Weights and Measures Laws, including packaging and net weight labeling laws. Some 29 are in the form of the model state weights and measures law prepared by the National

Conference on Weights and Measures of the United States.

Meat Inspection Laws. Some of these may be pre-empted in certain provisions by the Federal Wholesome Meat Inspection Act of 1967. Others are in the process of change in the light of that statute.

This syllabus does not include local health or other food laws or ordinances which cover the manufacture and sale of margarine along with that of other foods. Nor does it include laws dealing with such matters as labor, transportation, and trade practices. (Legal citations are in Appendix A).

FEDERAL LAWS

The *Federal Margarine Act of 1950* is, of course, the most important national statute. Essentially, it is a comprehensive amendment to the Oleomargarine Act of 1886 as amended in 1902, 1930, and in 1931. It abolished the structure of taxes and licensing that had been established in the earlier laws and which had been administered by the old Bureau of Internal Revenue. It left only a 15 cents per pound import tax on oleomargarine to be collected by the Treasury Department under the Internal Revenue Code.

In the place of the revenue structure the Act of 1950 amended the Federal Food, Drug, and Cosmetic Act in three ways that primarily concerned colored margarine. Section 301 of the latter law was expanded by adding a new paragraph ("m") to include among prohibited acts the sale of colored margarine in violation of a new Section 407.

This new section in turn was inserted to set forth certain requirements of colored margarine packaging and labeling, and its notification in public eating places. Finally, Section 402 of the food law was expanded, adding a new paragraph ("e") to place under the regular classification of adulterated food any margarine or butter unfit for food use.

These new powers of course were to be enforced by the U. S. Food and Drug Administration. On April 13, 1950, that agency, acting under the new law, published interpretative labeling regulations to clarify the law's application in various details. This applied, with certain distinctions, to both colored and uncolored margarine. The same agency also issued a clarifying statement on how public eating places could comply with the rather cumbersome new federal provisions regarding notification when colored margarine is served.

The 1950 Act placed margarine on a wholly if special regulatory basis under the pure food laws. Further, it provided for the regulation of margarine advertising by placing in the Federal Trade Commission the authority to act against the use of any representations in such promotions that might cause the consumer to buy it as a dairy product. This was accomplished by adding to the Federal Trade Commission Act, Subsections 15 (a), (2) and 15 (f). In so doing, Congress inserted in the Act (Section 5) unusually severe penalties for violation of any FTC order involving any article. This law's application has been withheld in cases where dairy terms are used to describe flavor and other product attributes.

None of these executive agency regulations, nor the 1950 Act itself, have been challenged in the courts.

For the first time in Federal law, the 1950 Act gave sanction to the word "margarine" by fully equating it with the older term "oleomargarine." Its definition of the colored product was necessarily broader than that already established in the Federal Standard, which was amended in 1952 to permit the labeled product name to be "margarine."

The *Federal Food, Drug, and Cosmetic Act,* as amended, embraces margarine along with other foods, and specifically in the amendments made by the Margarine Act of 1950 as described. Standards of the Food and Drug Administration for margarine (or oleomargarine) and for liquid margarine have been established under this law. Two amendments—the color additives law of 1960 and the food additives law of 1958—relate to margarine ingredients and other matters.

The *Wholesome Meat Act of 1967* updated the meat inspection authority that since 1906 had included margarine made in substantial part with animal fat and had been administered by the United States Department of Agriculture.[3]

The 1967 statute continued the coverage of margarine or oleomargarine within the context of its widened powers of USDA enforcement. The disparity between FDA and USDA margarine inspection procedures was therefore not changed, although the new law looked to increasing uniformity between the two agencies' food regulatory functions.

The Agriculture Department's Standard and other regulations for margarine also continue to be separate from the FDA Standard and margarine regulations, but with no real difference in provisions as of the most recent revision.

The Fair Packaging and Labeling Act of 1966 applies to margarine as to other retail products. Labeling regulations issued under it by the Food and Drug Administration add, in certain respects, to the other federal laws. The regulations also specifically exempt margarine from certain provisions of the act.

National policy concerning margarine has been set by Congress principally in the form of these federal statutes. As a group, they reflect the shift established by the Act of 1950 from prohibitive restrictionism to "normal" regulation, utilizing existing or general consumer protection legislation and enforcement agencies.

The changeover has not been entirely completed. The restrictionist policy continues to get expression, though on a different basis. Mainly it secures authorizations for the disposal of quantities of government-purchased butter, acquired under the price support system, through institutional markets that otherwise would go to margarine on a commercial price basis.

The federal government's administration of some programs is conducted with inequitable results where margarine is concerned. Margarine is not price-supported, although the major oilseed sources (soybeans, cottonseed, corn) of its vegetable oils are, and also the nonfat milk powder it uses. The animal fat ingredient lard is price-aided by export or other subsidy or purchase; in 1969 this greatly reduced its availability for low-cost margarine. Vegetable oils also have been the object of price-aiding export programs. Margarine has been included in certain federal food donations programs only on a temporary basis, by commercial purchase to meet limited requirements. Defense Department procurement of margarine for direct armed services use is reduced when surplus butter is available[4] at the expense of the government's price support program. (Commisaries and PX stores offer margarine as they do other foods.)

An oddity in the whole system is the omission by Congress of margarine in the list of foods in the Navy Ration Code. The Navy and its related services are thereby forbidden to serve the spread at table mess, though they have requested removal of the restriction since 1951.

State Laws

Forty-seven of the fifty states had laws in 1969 that specifically applied to margarine or margarine-like products. These laws mostly go back many years, some more than half a century, although nearly all have been modified considerably by amendment or interpretation from time to time. As a result, their provisions bear some similarities in content and, sometimes, in language.

Thus, all states have come to permit yellow margarine, the last two to act being Minnesota (1963) and Wisconsin (1967). Most of the old excise taxes on the product have been removed. Some repeat the federal law's language or refer to it. Most contain some type of definition or language concerning composition.

Many states vest enforcement in state agricultural agencies where margarine regulation is often administered in conjunction with dairy affairs. Nearly all state laws contain language more or less detailing regulatory and punitive authorizations. Many contain a bar against the use of dairy terms in labeling, but often the language is not uniform and the application is not entirely clear.

While considerable degree of uniformity has been achieved in margarine state laws, diversity remains a basic problem, as has been noted in connection with labeling. Composition requirements also show some variations between states.

Put together, the special margarine state laws make a sizable volume. To report them in detail in this space is not feasible. The more concise method is followed, in the summary below, of identifying only the major provisions in each state that materially affect marketing or composition *and* that are not identical or practically so with the federal law, which has already been described. The bulk of the language in the laws' provisions that is reasonably consistent with the federal law (such as permitting yellow margarine or labeling) is omitted in the interest of simplicity, as are those provisions concerned with authorizations and administration.

The person interested in the detailed application of these laws will, of course, want to examine their texts. They are subject to periodic change by legislatures. Moreover the restrictive provisions (taxing or labeling) are continually up for legislative review and removal.

The following summary of state laws is based on the texts, the *Compilation of Federal and State Laws on Margarine* and on analyses made available by the National Association of Margarine Manufacturers, the organization principally concerned with this area of food regulatory law.

Summary of Provisions of State Margarine Laws That Affect Marketing or Composition and Are Not Uniform With the Federal Law

Alabama. Fortification minimum for vitamin A is 9,000 U.S.P. units per pound. Retail sale only in units of ¼, ½, 1, or multiples of 1 pound.

Alaska. Retail sale only in units of ¼, ½, 1, or multiples of 1 pound.

Arkansas. Special requirements for product name labeling and for notification when colored margarine is served in public eating places.

California. Public eating places may not serve yellow margarine unless the patron requests it, and in any case, must be licensed annually ($2). Special requirement for notification when colored margarine is served in public eating places. Manufacturers must be licensed annually ($100). Retail sale in units of ¼, ½, or 1 pound only. Restriction on state institutional use.

Colorado. All margarine is taxable at 10 cents a pound unless composed of certain named fats of domestic origin. Wholesalers and manufacturers must be licensed annually ($25). Only milk or milk products may be used to flavor. Special requirements for product name labeling and when colored margarine is served in public eating places. Retail sale in packages of less than 5 pounds only.

Delaware. Special requirements for product name labeling and when yellow margarine is served in public eating places.

District of Columbia. The federal law applies.

Florida. Laws pertaining to "imitiation butter" may not apply to margarine. A state court held yellow margarine not prohibited from sale under an imitation butter statute [*Mayo v. Winn & Lovett Grocery Co.*, 19 So. 2d 867 (1944)].

Georgia. Retail sale in units of 1 pound only. [Georgia has no special margarine law].

Hawaii. Two general requirements dealing with product name labeling.

Idaho. State institutions and schools prohibited from using margarine when surplus butter is available to them but a physician may order it to be used. Special requirement for notification if yellow margarine is used for cooking or served in public eating places.

Illinois. A unique requirement is that the ingredient statement have the artificial flavoring or coloring in bold type. Retail sale in units of ¼, ½, 1, or multiples of 1 pound only.

Indiana. Special requirements for labeling product name and manufacturer's identification, and for notification when yellow margarine is served in public eating places.

Iowa. Special requirement for product name labeling.

Kansas. All margarine is taxable at 10 cents a pound unless composed of certain named ingredient fats. Special notification requirement when yellow margarine is served in public eating places.

Louisiana. Fortification minimum for vitamin A is 9,000 U.S.P. units per pound.

Maine. Special requirement for labeling the product name and the name and address of the seller, and for notification when yellow margarine is served in public eating places. Retail sale in units of ¼, ½, 1 or multiples of 1 pound only.

Maryland. Special requirements for notification where margarine is sold and when used for cooking or served in public eating places. Retail sale in units of ¼, ½, 1, or multiples of 1 pound only.

Massachusetts. Retailers licensed annually (50 cents). Special requirements for notification when yellow margarine is served in public eating places.

Michigan. Public schools may serve margarine only if attending physician or dietician recommends. Servings of yellow margarine in public eating places require triangular pats and special notification. Retail sale in units of ¼, ½, 1 or multiples of 1 pound.

Minnesota. All yellow margarine is taxed 10 cents a pound. Manufacturers annually licensed ($5). State institutions may serve margarine only on superintendent's order and physician's direction for specific patients. Special requirement for notification when yellow margarine is served in public eating places. Margarine may be sold retail only in units of 1 pound or more.

Mississippi. Fortification minimum for vitamin A is 9,000 U.S.P. units per pound. Special requirements for labeling the product name and when yellow margarine is served in public eating places. Retail sale in units of ¼, ½, 1 or multiples of 1 pound only.

Missouri. Special requirement for notification when yellow margarine is served in public eating places. Retail sale in units of ¼, ½, 1 or multiples of 1 pound.

Montana. Wholesaler licensed annually ($20); also manufacturers by a sliding scale. Special product name labeling requirement. Retail sale only in units of 1 or 2 pounds.

Nebraska. Retailers, wholesalers, and manufacturers annually licensed ($3, $25, and $100, respectively). Certain state institutions prohibited from using. Special notification requirement when yellow margarine is served in public eating places.

Nevada. Special requirements for product labeling and when yellow margarine is served in public eating places. Retail sale in units of ¼, ½, 1, 1½, or multiples of 1 pound.

New Hampshire. Special product name labeling requirement.

New Jersey. Special labeling requirement for sellers' identification.

New Mexico. Retail sale in units of ¼, ½, 1, or multiples of 1 pound only.

New York. Special notification requirements when yellow margarine is possessed in a form ready for serving or served in public eating places which must also be annually licensed ($10). Retail sale in units of ¼, ½, 1 or multiples of 1 pound.

North Carolina. All margarine is taxable at 10 cents a pound unless it is composed of certain domestic fats. Special requirement for notification when yellow margarine is served in public eating places. Retail sale is in units of ¼, ½, 1½, or multiples of 1 pound.

North Dakota. Yellow margarine is taxed 10 cents a pound. Wholesalers and manufacturers are annually licensed ($5 and $10, respectively). State institutions may not buy margarine but may use it if donated. Special notification requirement when yellow margarine used for cooking or in public eating places. Sale in units of no less than 1 nor more than 30 pounds. Special product name labeling requirement.

Ohio. Special requirements for labeling and when yellow margarine is used for cooking or served in eating places.

Oklahoma has no separate margarine law.

Oregon. Special requirement for notification when yellow margarine is served in public eating places. Retail sale in units of ¼, ½, 1, or multiples of 1 pound only.

Pennsylvania. Retail sale in units of ¼, ½, 1, or multiples of 1 pound only.

Puerto Rico and *other U. S. Territories.* The federal law applies.

Rhode Island. Special product name labeling requirement.

South Carolina. Fortification minimum for vitamin A is 9,000 U.S.P. units per pound. Margarine is taxed 10 cents per pound unless composed of certain named domestic fats. Manufacturers licensed annually ($10).

South Dakota. Yellow margarine taxed 10 cents a pound until July 1, 1971. Special notification requirements when yellow margarine is kept, used for cooking, or served in public eating places. Wholesalers and manufacturers licensed annually ($5).

Tennessee. Fortification minimum for vitamin A is 15,000 U.S.P. units per pound; vitamin D, 2,000 units; there is a state assay, with fees. All margarine is taxable at 10 cents a pound unless it is composed of certain named domestic fats. Special requirements for labeling product name and ingredients statement, and when yellow margarine is used for cooking or served in public eating places. Retail sale in units of ¼, ½, 1 or multiples of 1 pound only. Since 1949 there has been a state Standard, identical to the federal Food and Drug Administration Standard.

Texas. Fortification minimum for vitamin A is 9,000 U.S.P. units per pound. Special product name and ingredients labeling requirement. Retail sale in units of ¼, ½, 1, or 1½ pounds or multiples of 1 pound only.

Utah. Yellow margarine is taxed 10 cents per pound; white, 5 cents. Retail sale in units of ¼, ½, 1, 1½ or multiples of 1 pound only. All persons dealing in margarine must be licensed (no fee).

Vermont. Retailers are annually licensed ($2) and wholesalers also (a sliding scale). Special notification requirement when yellow margarine is served in a public eating place.

Virginia. Special notification requirement when yellow margarine is used for cooking or served in public eating places.

Washington. Margarine use by state institutions prohibited unless the product is donated by the Federal government. Retail sale in units of ¼, ½, 1 or multiples of 1 pound only.

West Virginia. Retail sale only by weight; special net weight labeling requirement.

Wisconsin. All yellow margarine is taxed 5¼ cents per pound; the tax, enacted in 1967, was enacted as a temporary levy to expire in 1972. Yellow margarine may be served in public eating places only if the patron requests it. State institutions may use margarine only on the superintendent's order and physician's direction for health reasons pertaining to a specific patient. Schools may not use margarine. Retail sale in 1-pound units only.

Wyoming. Special notification requirement if yellow margarine is used for cooking or served in public eating places.

LABELING AND PACKAGING

The labeling on the margarine package is governed by five different federal laws. Most states also have laws regulating the food's labeling. Under these requirements the principal items of information for which the consumer looks are each stated in a certain way or ways, whether the labeling is on the carton or the inner wrapper.

The basic mandatory information under federal law (exclusive of certain exceptions in detail) is as follows:

1. *The product name* can be only "margarine" or "oleomargarine" (or, "liquid margarine" or "liquid oleomargarine"). It must appear on each label panel likely to be displayed, and parallel to the base on which the package rests. The name must be in letters at least as large and bold as other corresponding letters on the label. On inner units the letter must be at least as large as 20-point type (slightly more than ¼-inch).

2. *All ingredients* must appear in conjunction with the product wherever it is shown, without intervening material. All ingredients must be declared in order of decreasing predominance in the margarine. Some have special labeling requirements:

Fats and oils, if they are hydrogenated, must be so labeled. The usual declaration lists them as "partially hardened" or "partially hydrogenated."

Vitamins (A and D) must be declared in terms of federally established minimum daily requirements for adults in proportion to a specified serving. In addition, the minimum daily requirement information for children and the total amount of vitamin added to margarine is often declared.

Other ingredients are required to be declared by specific common names listed in the federal margarine Standards. No variation in these names is permitted, except for artificial coloring and flavoring ingredients, which may be declared by a general phrase such as "artificially colored."

3. *Net weight* must appear conspicuously on the label in a type size determined by the area of the principal display panel. On all one-pound cartons of margarine it is at least ⅛ inch in height; larger sizes are customary.

4. The *manufacturer* or distributor or packer must be identified along with his city and "zip" code.

The U. S. Department of Agriculture requires that a notice pertaining to federal meat inspection appear on all margarines which contain animal fat in substantial part: "U. S. Inspected and Passed."

Package weight (and, therefore, general size) is also regulated by federal and state laws. The 1950 federal law requires that colored margarine sold at retail be packed in units of 1 pound or less. Many state requirements follow this, and five states have a one-pound minimum.

However, as is shown by the summary of state law provisions in the preceding section (which describes the package weight provisions of those state laws that differ from the federal law in this respect), there is a good deal of variation at the state level.

Although by 1970 15 states had adopted the "model state law" on weights and measures, which permits the retail sale of margarine in units of ¼, ½, 1, and multiples of 1 pound, no retail margarine is marketed in more than the one-pound size because of the federal limitation. Margarine package styles have not proliferated very much. Thus their contents and weights are recognizable by the consumer by their familiar size and shape.

PRINCIPAL COURT DECISIONS

Any description of the laws relating to margarine would be
incomplete without some mention of the judicial interpretations
that have followed margarine legislation. Though historical in
their context, they have contributed to the present status of laws
relating not only to margarine but to other products.

The subject may be most conveniently reviewed by means of
a classification of the principal issues with which the courts
were confronted. Necessarily, it is selective; many details of the
opinions concerned are omitted.[5]

1. *Approval of Federal Taxation*

The constitutionality of the first federal taxes on "oleomargarine" that featured the Act of 1886 was a matter of serious
doubt in Congress as well as in the White House. President
Cleveland signed the restrictive measure only after disclaim-
ing his responsibility to consider any Congressional intent beyond the statute's stated objective of raising revenue. In time
this view was shared by the United States Supreme Court, although the question was not settled until the final decision in
the case of *In re Kollock* in 1897.

Citing earlier precedent, the Court recognized the prohibitive
nature of the two cents per pound tax levied by the Act, but
held that the taxing power could indeed be used oppressively
if it were otherwise valid. The Oleomargarine Act, the Court
held, was on its face a revenue measure and the judiciary would
not look for other motives.

When in 1904 the constitutionality of the second federal
oleomargarine tax step—the carefully worded 1902 amendment
which applied a near-prohibitive tax of ten cents a pound on
yellow-colored oleomargarine—came before the Court, the latter
again refused to go beyond the stated revenue objective. *McCray
v. United States* found that the 5th amendment's guarantee of
property rights did not prevent Congress from enacting a revenue measure that could destroy a business.

The McCray case later became a firm precedent on the subject of federal tax power and legislative intent. Under its broad shelter the oleomargarine revenue system became entrenched until Congress repealed the tax provisions in 1950.

During the 1920's there appeared all-vegetable yellow-colored cooking compounds. A technical error in the Acts of 1886 and 1902 ("vegetable oil annatto" appeared with an unnecessary comma—"vegetable oil, annato") seemed to exempt these products from the category of butter substitutes and thereby opened a gap in the margarine revenue system. In 1924 the Supreme Court held them exempt in *Higgins Manufacturing Co. v. Page;* other cases followed suit. Not until 1930 was the issue resolved when Congress again amended the law to redefine oleomargarine to include such compounds.

2. Disapproval of Total Prohibition

Opposition within Congress turned back repeated efforts to enact a federal law totally prohibiting oleomargarine. Some states, however, did pass such measures. A series of cases before the Supreme Court and the highest courts of several states pointed out the question of the constitutionality of such laws, flatly barring the manufacture or sale of the food regardless of color or ingredients.

In a famous early oleomargarine decision, *People v. Marx,* in 1885, the New York Court of Appeals declared the state prohibition invalid. It viewed the law's intent as outright economic protectionism. But when the issue came before the Supreme Court three years later, the decision was reversed. In *Powell v. Pennsylvania,* the Court refused to question the legislature's judgment as to the measures necessary to safeguard public health, In a much-quoted dissent Mr. Justice Field posed the public question of why a new product, serviceable to consumers, should be permitted to be so restricted.

The Powell case did not rule on the validity of prohibiting the sale of oleomargarine brought in from another state in interstate commerce. This aspect was not the subject of an opinion until 1898 when the Supreme Court considered *Schollen-berger v. Pennsylvania*. Under the same Pennsylvania statute, the Court found the prohibition was not valid when applied to oleomargarine "imported" in its original package. This decision, a part of the "original package" controversy of that era, was resolved for oleomargarine in the Act of 1902 whereby Congress divested the product of the protection of interstate commerce when it was transported into a prohibiting state.

3. *Approval of State Prohibitions of Yellow-Colored Margarine*

By imposing a higher federal tax on yellow-colored oleomargarine in 1902 Congress in effect had created a separate legal definition of this product. Before then, in the 1894 case of *Plumley v. Massachusetts*, the Supreme Court approved a state law that prohibited the manufacture and sale of margarine colored yellow. The Schollenberger case followed the same view. But in the same year as the latter case, in another opinion, *Collins v. New Hampshire*, the Court struck down a law that, by requiring margarine to be sold in pink-colored form, was tantamount to a prohibition.

Years after, in 1927, a further limit to prohibitory efforts was set by the Wisconsin Supreme Court. In *J. F. Jelke Co. v. Emery*, that court declared void a law which barred margarine containing milk in combination with any "oil"—also tantamount to a prohibition.

4. *Approval of State Margarine Taxes*

Not surprisingly, state taxes on the product were upheld by the same reasoning that had been given to approve the 1886 and 1902 federal taxes. The courts abstained from questioning purposes or motives other than the one stated in such laws: raising revenue. Margarine taxes thus became established as a valid exercise of state taxation powers. This situation encouraged the enactment of new state margarine taxes in the 1930's. It made the removal of such taxes feasible only by legislative action, thus transferring a consumer matter into the difficult and foreign sphere of state financing.

The United States Supreme Court in 1924 upheld such a tax in a landmark decision involving a 15 cents per pound margarine levy enacted by the State of Washington, *Magnano Co. v. Hamilton*. Ten years later the South Dakota Supreme Court held valid its state's 10 cents per pound tax in *Schmitt v. Nord*.

The courts also have upheld state laws which classified all margarine for taxation, but which included exemptions for margarines identified as composed of fats and oils specified in the statutes. This became a favorite device during the 1930's to force the use of domestic fats and oils such as cottonseed oil. In 1936, in *Coy v. Linder,* the Georgia Supreme Court approved a tax law that so exempted margarines made with specified domestic fats. However, in 1945 the Nebraska Supreme Court found a margarine taxing statute to be unreasonable when it exempted only those margarines containing more than half domestic animal fats and no imported fats (*Thorin v. Burke*).

5. *Federal Standard Upheld*

An important case in margarine legal history is *Land O' Lakes Creameries, Inc. v. McNutt*. The U. S. Food and Drug Administration, acting under new and significant standard-making powers granted by Congress in 1938, had promulgated its original Definition and Standard of Identity for Oleomargarine in 1941. The Standard in effect re-identified margarine for the purposes of federal regulation as "oleomargarine"—an entity different from "imitation butter" and other outmoded names. The Federal Court of Appeals upheld this action and thereby preserved the Standard.

In 1966 a product labeled "imitation margarine" that resembled margarine but was not composed according to the Standard was seized by the Food and Drug Administration as not being in compliance with the 80 per cent minimum fat requirement and the ingredients limitations in the Standard. In *United States v. 856 Cases . . . "Demi,"* etc., a Federal District

Court rejected the agency's contention that, under the 1950 Margarine Act, all products in semblence of butter were "margarine" and as such must conform to the Standard. The Court decided that margarine was not necessarily the only "imitation butter" and that there could be an "imitation margarine." The decision was not appealed. Lowfat margarines are accordingly labeled "imitation margarine" and are produced without a Standard.

6. *Limitation of "Dairy Terms" Usage*

One provision of the 1950 Margarine amended the Federal Trade Commission Act's Section 15(a) (2) to require that margarine advertisements be considered to constitute "false advertising" if representations are made or suggested that the margarine is a dairy product.

The practical effect of this provision was to make legally questionable the use of any dairy or "farm" terminology in margarine advertising or promotion, regardless of the truthfulness of such reference. While the general meaning and purpose is apparent, the delimitation of when and under what conditions a given term is subject to this provision has recently changed.

In 1954 the Federal Trade Commission found certain terminology to be prohibited, and this position was affirmed by a federal Court of Appeals in *E. F. Drew & Co. Inc. v. F.T.C.* In *Reddi-Spred Corp. v. F.T.C.* two years later, another federal Court of Appeals also affirmed the Commission's bar against advertising that highlighted dairy ingredients, such as milk in a margarine. Other decisions under the dairy terms provision have prohibited the listing of margarine in store advertisements under dairy words of one kind or another.

In 1969 and 1970 the Commission modified these stands when it refused to act against advertisements comparing margarines with butter or describing buttery flavor.

From the above very brief synopsis it is evident that margarine law—the whole body of which embraces many more judicial and administrative decisions—has changed in response

to the times. The restrictionist type of law is no longer acceptable. Further improvements are likely to come in the interest
of greater uniformity and in line with the contemporary interest
in improved legislation affecting consumers.

1. Since about 1942 the following withdrawals of legal restrictions on margarine took place; removal of federal taxes (1950); removal of 29 state
prohibitions of colored margarine; repeal of 19 state special taxes on the
product; removal of other restrictions in 32 states.

The margarine legal restrictions existing as of June 1, 1970, are listed in the
table on page 153.

2. For example: Phillip Tocker, "Trade Barriers," in the *Texas Law Review*,
XVIII, 280 (April, 1940); W. F. Pabst, Jr., "Interstate Trade Barriers and
State Oleomargarine Taxes," *Southern Economic Journal*, VII, 505-517 (April,
1941); F. E. Melder, "Interstate Tax Barriers," in *Proceedings of the 51st National Tax Conference . . .* (Harrisburg, 1958), 285-86.

Those products variously known as "filled" or "imitation" dairy foods have
also been the object of restrictive federal and state laws, in a manner and
for reasons comparable to the old margarine barriers. Margarine's example is
often cited as that of the harbinger for the eventual importance of these other
products that are prepared to supplement ice cream and other dairy foods at
lower cost.

3. Margarine subject to the jurisdiction of the U. S. Department of Agriculture is that which is determined by the Secretary to be a "meat food product," *i.e., a* margarine containing animal fat "in substantial part" (9 C.F.R.
§301.1(w)). This may be a minimum of about 10 per cent.

4. Defense procurement of margarine, opposed by those seeking government
outlets for butter, calls up periodic echoes in Congress of the old struggle to
end taxes on the spread. For one example, see *Congressional Record,* July 11,
1966, pages 14382-83.

5. The subject is treated for the pre-1929 period in Katharine Snodgrass,
Margarine as a Butter Substitute (Stanford, 1930), and more fully and up
to 1935 in Anne DeWees, *State and Federal Legislation and Decisions Relating to Oleomargarine* (Washington, 1936). A useful survey is J. K. Mallory,
Jr., "The Oleomargarine Controversy," in *Virginia Law Review*, XXXIII, 636-
40 (September, 1947). There is occasional comment in law reviews and elsewhere.

History

"I always thought the tax on margarine was wrong!" exclaimed President Harry S. Truman when he placed his signature on the Margarine Act of 1950, thus putting a dramatic end to sixty-five years of federal restrictions on the spread.[1] His forthright opinion was that of one who had seen the food sold in his midwestern town as a lowly substitute and then gradually rise in status. He was a politician and margarine had been a subject of political controversy for a long time.

Its record is a unique one of legislative intervention to repress one product in order to protect a competitor. This fact dominated margarine history from 1886 to 1953. While national issues of war and peace arose, flourished, and vanished into the archives, margarine battles went on and on. The story of those battles is worth relating.[2]

BEGINNINGS

The starting point is December 30, 1873, the date the first American patent was granted to the originator of a primitive "oleomargarine."[3] It was a French invention deliberately undertaken to provide a butter-like food that the nation required because of butter shortages during the Napoleonic wars.

The inventor, Hippolyte Mège, was born on October 24, 1817, in the venerable town of Draguignan in eastern Provence.[4] Later he added to his name that of his mother's family, Mouriés or Mouriéz.

Mège early entered the profession of pharmacy—no minor calling, for French pharmacists had importantly contributed to the brilliant achievements of chemistry.[5] Soon he received the first of various awards for his discoveries and eventually he achieved recognition by the National Academy of Science. He became preoccupied with the vision of scientifically improved foods affording better nutrition and lower cost.

French national power and growing industry at that time required a more secure food supply. The French poor and those in other European countries lived on a subsistence level. Fats were frequently lacking. Butter often was excluded by its cost, as van Gogh vividly illustrated in his famous painting "The Potato Eaters."

This situation impressed Emperior Louis Napoleon III when butter came to be in chronically short supply for his soldiers and sailors.[6] Following French precedent, he offered a prize for the invention of a substitute. Attempts to create butter-like substances had been made for years. A basis had been laid by the great chemist Michel Eugène Chevreul, a pioneer in fat chemistry, who in 1813 gave the name "margarine" to a fatty acid component he had isolated and which became identified as "margaric acid."[7]

Mège came up with what he called "oleo-margarine," attaching "oleo" (beef fat) to Chevreul's "margaric," because the Mège product was composed of the fat from cattle.

Mège's creation reasonably suited the Emperor's purposes. His real contribution was a method of flavoring by mixing the fat with milk and other substances.[8] In his view he had invented not a substitute but a less expensive form of butter with what was then considered purity and nutritional value. Mège won the prize and on July 17, 1869, applied for French and English patents. He set up a factory in Paris and began production with the benefit of official sanction.[9] The new food soon began to be produced in other European countries.[10]

Although Mège's factories failed and he died obscurely, margarine began to take hold in northern Europe and the United States during the 1880's.

For the sake of simplicity this history will refer to margarine although oleomargarine was the common name until World War II and the federally defined name until 1951.

AMERICAN BEGINNINGS

Just when margarine began to be commercially manufactured in the United States may never be precisely dated. News of Mège's invention apparently spurred experiments aimed to create fats from edible meat fats. The first of a stream of "butter substitute" patents was issued on January 3, 1871. One is reported to have been used by a firm in 1873.

Within another year the first Mège American patent had been issued and production undertaken sometime before 1876 by the United States Dairy Company at New York. The firm's chemist, Henry C. Mott, Jr., introduced improvements. He called his product "artificial butter." It contained, he said, "nothing foreign to the very best of [dairy] butter."[11]

By 1881 U. S. Dairy had a subsidiary, the Commercial Manufacturing Company, running full blast in a large barn of a plant situated at the west end of 48th Street. Smoking chimneys and rumbling drays proclaimed that a sizeable business was going on, very possibly several million pounds being sold annually. An unknown writer praised "this great discovery." "The markets in this city are full of oleomargarine," he reported, "it commands a high price from its intrinsic merits . . . has driven rancid butter from the market. The new oleomargarine being without buttermilk, has keeping qualities that recommend it."[12]

In that year some fifteen plants across the country were already operating and perhaps affiliated with Commercial. By 1886 the number of surviving factories was reported to be thirty-four. "Oleomargarine is a fact in the commercial world and must be treated as such," exulted the *Scientific American*. Led by Armour and Company in 1883, national meat packers entered the business. It is estimated that by 1880 the young industry enjoyed a capitalization of about $1.7 million with a production value of nearly $7 million.[13] It was fast coming of age.

However crude these first margarines were by modern standards, they seem to have caught on and were deemed as good as average-grade butter. Their cost was about a third below that

(Batchelor in the New York Daily News)

of the dairy spread. There existed a genuine need for a low-
cost table spread. Most Americans consumed much plain bread
and potatoes. Butter was generously used, and much was of
lower quality.

A serious problem arose in the sale of the new spread. Most
food staples were sold from bulk containers; shopkeepers ladled
margarine and butter from a tub. In those cracker-barrel days,
the sale of foods adulterated on the premises if not elsewhere
was not uncommon. It easily involved margarine.[14]

DEVELOPING ATTITUDES

Adulteration became a well-publicized problem, providing the
rationale for regulative laws and an excuse for punitive laws
that followed. Anti-margarine propaganda by dairying interests
colorfully exaggerated the situation. Pure food protagonists
recognized it as a part of the general food control situation
and urged truth-in-packaging-and-labeling.

A question in margarine's history is why this condition went
on more or less for years despite sensible, widely stated proposals both within and outside the industry for regulatory
legislation that, as later experience showed, would have pro-
tected consumers. The explanation seems to be in a combination
of the national food adulteration problem, the failure to
establish pure food laws until 1906, and the contemporary
position of the organized dairy industry—plus much public in-
difference.

To most Americans of that day "consumers" hardly existed.
An exception was Dr. Harvey W. Wiley, the leader of the pure
food fight. In 1883 he headed the first government food regulating agency. In company with others dealing with public
health problems he regarded margarine as a worthwhile food
that exemplified the need for food legislation to protect consumers.

For margarine the answer was well thought out—a limited-
weight, well-labeled retail package. Well before 1900 it was urged
vigorously by (among others) the highly regarded Rep. James

W. Wadsworth, of upstate New York's dairy region, onetime Chairman of the House Agriculture Committee.[15]

State laws requiring identification had begun with New York and Maryland in 1877; there were seventeen by 1886. But these attempts did not prevent bulk sale. Soon the long anti-margarine effort in politics commenced. It hardened emotionally. Intemperate assertions and claims against margarine were capped by the President of the American Agricultural and Dairy Association who demanded the "total extermination of imitation butter."[16]

The adversary movement against it imbued many Americans with misconceptions about margarine and hurt its public image and acceptance. Mark Twain, fearing the artificiality he saw about him, thought margarine one symbol of it.[17]

The margarine manufacturers and their allies could not successfully combat the political strength of their opponents. Meanwhile, margarine was gaining in sales. Cottonseed oil began to be incorporated as a liquid ingredient to achieve a softer spread about 1875. New York City was the leading market, taking nearly a fourth of national production. The *Agricultural Chemist* in 1879 reported that "carefully prepared oleomargarine" was "superior to poor butter as regards taste, odor, and healthfulness." In 1881 the New York City Board of Health declared that no one of scientific standing had found it otherwise than "palatable and wholesome . . . a most valued article of food."[18]

By the end of the product's first full decade, it had acquired a mixed set of attitudes toward it—some favorable, some antagonistic. It possessed also a sales potential—and a powerful opponent.

RESTRICTIONISM

These conflicting attitudes toward margarine crystallized amidst the panic of 1873, the first great agricultural depression, and the rise of militant dairy organizations.

There were at least sixteen state regulatory laws by 1886 to control margarine's sale. They were not being effectively enforced.[19] Proposals to regulate "butter substitutes" began to be

heard in Congress. Nothing happening, some states were persuaded to enact radical legislation that split off from the pure
food concept and flatly prohibited the competitor spread. New
York led the way in 1884. Six states followed by 1886. By 1897
five other states had followed suit and other types of control
had appeared.

When a court voided the New York ban in 1885[20] federal
intervention became the goal. After a heated battle, Congress
passed the Margarine Act of 1886. As finally enacted it constituted a compromise that satisfied nobody. A tax of two cents
a pound was imposed. Manufacturers and dealers were to be
regulated by licenses, the costs being $600 for manufacturers,
$480 for wholesalers, and $48 for retailers—the last two high
enough to set up a trade barrier. President Grover Cleveland,
from New York's dairy upstate, signed the law as a revenue
measure.[21]

The arguments for and against foreshadowed those of the long
political conflict ahead. The "workingman's butter" was defended as necessary to lower income families, an important market
for the livestock industry, and a farm product. Its health
properties were stoutly defended. The constitutionality of any
restriction was questioned. Proponents talked of fraudulent
sale, impure ingredients, and special protection for the dairy
industry. All this had been heard before and would be heard in
Congress as late as 1950.[22]

The 1886 law was a failure. Though it did recognize margarine
as a legitimate article of interstate commerce, the law con-
strained sales by the high dealer's license costs. The problem of
identification at point of sale had not been solved (labeling only
of the bulk tub was required). The Act's inadequacies proved
that the taxation route was only a subterfuge for favored-com-
petitor legislation. Establishing the federal tax on this one food
scored a victory for margarine's opponents but neglected the
need for the pure food type of regulation.

The Act of 1886 reflected its times. It was not the result of
solid agricultural unity. Its philosophy of governmental intervention was favored by some business elements as well as some

agrarian organizations. Margarine after 1900 found allies among the cattlemen and cottonseed interests, but even before then the southern Grange and populists seem to have been lukewarm about the dairy-based attack. Agriculture and business alike were seeking new forms of government protection in laws which, in a sense, the 1886 Act previewed—the Interstate Commerce Act the next year, and the Sherman Antitrust Act and the Tariff Act of 1890.

The Yellow Wall

Now the states had to revise their prohibitory laws. As they did so, often going to extremes, the U. S. Supreme Court became an historic arbiter of margarine's destiny. In 1888 it decided that a state could not prohibit the sale of the food when made within its own borders. In 1897 it got around to the federal law and upheld it as a revenue measure, though acknowledging it to be an oppressive use of the tax power. In 1898 the Court determined that a state could not bar the sale of margarine brought within its borders and sold in the original package.[23]

Meanwhile the search for a legally defensible method of prohibition of margarine concentrated on color. The spread was then (as was much butter) colored with the vegetable substance annatto and (also like butter) it probably was not labeled as being artificially colored. The restrictionist brief on coloring evolved rather swiftly: that a lard-white appearance was a proper form of identification regardless of the natural colors given the product by any of the fats of which it might be composed or by the use of colorings as in other foods.

"We want to drive the oleomargarine manufacturers out of the business," asserted one protagonist for color restriction. Margarine protagonists refused to accept color pre-emption. "God Almighty," said one at a later date, "made dandelions, grass, and cows."[24]

Prohibitions of the manufacture and sale of yellow-colored margarine led off promptly in 1886, in New Jersey and New York. With one hand the Supreme Court upheld such laws in

1894, while with the other it struck down forced coloration
(pink) laws four years after.[25] By 1902 some thirty-two states,
or eighty per cent of the population, lived under color bans.
The torrent of bills and cases was unceasing. (As recently as
1967 a North Dakota legislator demanded that margarine be
colored pink or green.)

By 1903 a veritable Chinese wall had been erected against
margarine in general and the artificially colored product in
particular. Forced into new and arbitrary channels, consumption
in effect was re-directed—New York lost its plants by 1889.
Factories became fewer; controlling ownership often became
larger. Yet the demand for margarine pressed against the yellow
wall. Following a brief setback after the 1886 law to 35 million
pounds, production doubled by 1894, and by 1902 again set a
record of 126 million, or an average of about 1.6 pounds per
person.

The National Dairyman's Union predictably concluded that
something further must be done. To avoid the Supreme Court's
defense of interstate commerce, the new attack was for a higher
federal tax on yellow-colored margarine. Representative Grout of
Vermont, whose attitude toward margarine and city folks
resembled the uncompromising granite of his state, marshalled
the dairy forces. On the defense side, the newly formed National Livestock Association took up the margarine cause in the
name of beef fat. Some voices were raised in behalf of southern
cottonseed oil.

Two enactments resulted in 1902. One amended the 1886 law
to raise the color tax to ten cents, or about half the retail price,
while white margarine was taxed at a nominal ¼ cent and its
distributors were given less expensive license charges—$200 for
wholesalers and $6 for retailers.[26] A separate enactment clarified
the power of state laws to bar margarine even in its original
package.

The new taxes were "class legislation of the most dangerous
character," asserted the minority report.[27] It offered the now
familiar solution that would require margarine to be sold in one
or two-pound packages only, the original package to be labeled.

A World War II cartoon by Shoemaker

Another President from New York, Theodore Roosevelt,
approved the new law.

RECONSTRUCTION

The 1902 color tax inaugrated a new period of struggle for
margarine. Congress and state legislatures had limited its availability to consumers so as to require them to choose between
two unsatisfactory alternatives: uncolored margarine (which
had to be colored at home) and a higher tax-raised price that
often was not much less than butter's price. If the shopper desired margarine pre-colored like other foods, she must pay about
the amount of price again in a tax; in many states she could
not buy it at all. Few stores carried it; most were discouraged
by the high federal license cost.

The product was no longer just a food. It had become a
movement.

Congress in effect had encouraged bootlegging colored margarine as butter. The enforcement agency, the Bureau of Internal Revenue, became one of the law's most devoted critics.
Finding less money being taken in from the tax than had been
anticipated it regularly pleaded for revision but to no avail. As
consumer protection the margarine tax was not meant to
accomplish anything.

The Federal Treasury collected from consumers between 1886
and 1902 some $27 million in margarine taxes and, indirectly,
license charges. Between 1902 and 1950 the amount totaled
$159 million. What the government spent in administering
the difficult law, what consumers lost by being denied a product
free to develop competitively, and what farmers missed in
markets for their fats and oils is, of course, not calculable. State
taxes were additional.

Though proposals to replace the margarine taxes with packaging and labeling controls got nowhere, a step forward was the
Pure Food and Drug Act of 1906 which put federal muscle into
the old crusade against adulteration and mislabeling. The Meat
Inspection Act of the same year put the manufacture of all mar-

garine employing animal fats—the major ingredient—under a factory inspection system. One longer-range effect noted by an observer was to enhance margarine's acceptability and give it a "larger sale." [28] The tax system already had become superfluous.

Consumption took a dive from the 120 million pounds high of 1902, touching bottom at 48 million in 1904. It had been pushed back to the 1886 rate. The margarine makers sought their salvation in fierce competition and innovations. They shared the zestful entrepreneurial spirit of the age although subject to unique government controls. [29]

By 1906 sales demonstrated again that there was a public demand for margarine. Production attained a modest peak of about 130 million pounds in 1910—the spread had barely caught up with eight years of poulation growth. Even adding the ten cent federal tax, the cost difference between the two spreads began slowly to widen about 1910.

Important advances were the development of the individual one-pound retail package, bearing the warranty of a brand name, the protection of paraffined cardboard, and fixed identifying labeling. Unit packaging appears to have commenced with the wrapping of separate prints during the eighteen-nineties; the one-pound carton probably was introduced about 1904. Soon the old bulk method of sale was obsolete. The product relationship between producer and consumer became a direct one.

Another consumer convenience introduced about 1902 was enclosed coloring matter to help the homemaker do her own coloring job. Thereafter, armies of small boys or their fathers had the chore of coloring the white margarine that mother brought home from the store.

To by-pass the ten cent tax on artificial coloring, yellow palm oil was adopted until the government interpreted this to be taxable. A refining discovery helped cottonseed oil keep its natural yellow in margarine but this too was ruled taxable. "Every method known to science" had been tried to provide a legal tax-free yellow-colored margarine, declared an unsympathetic Congressional committee in 1913. [30]

Meanwhile the process of hydrogenation was introduced in

1915. Now margarine could achieve the necessary solidity at
room temperature without being tied to naturally hard fats.
Vegetable oils, especially native cottonseed oil, could be employed. A more significant market for American farmers was in
sight and a more desirable product texture could be achieved.

Turning Point, 1911-1920

Hopes were high in the press in late 1911 and early 1912 that
Congress at last was going to do something about the notorious
"oleo tax." The press rang with denunciations of the unfairness
of the law to consumers and farm producers, and reported the
healthfulness of margarine and the high cost of butter. "There
never had been a logical reason for the discriminatory legislation
against oleomargarine. It is as much a legitimate commodity as
lard, butter, cheese . . . the consumer as well as the producer,
is entitled to consideration," wrote an Iowa editor. Another
writer found the tax as unjust as the tea tax of King George
III. A number of scientists rose to the product's defense.[31]

The unenforceability of the tax law became an issue in Congress. The Commissioner of Internal Revenue urged limiting
retail package sizes and reducing or removing the 10 cents tax.
"Had the tax," he complained in 1911, been only two cents the
nation's coffer would have been wealthier "by a large sum."[32]
Neither his nor other proposals got anywhere. Though pro-
gressivists had made use of the pure food cause, they virtually
ignored the margarine issue. Reform leadership rested with
men such as Senator "Fighting Bob" Robert M. LaFollette of
dairy Wisconsin and Senator Albert J. Beveridge of rural
Indiana, who could not have safely befriended margarine if
they had wished to.

Margarine[33] nevertheless had received favorable press exposure and free advertising and in 1913 use attained a new
record of 142 million pounds. By the beginning of 1917 margarine
was beginning to move into a rate of per person consumption of
2.2 pounds, double that of 1902-1909.

The leading margarine tax relief champion, the influential

Senator Oscar W. Underwood of cotton-producing Alabama, re-opened the tax issue, stressing the consumer—"The poor man who is struggling for his daily bread must eat white . . . oleomargarine, and you want to make it as distasteful to him as you can," he exclaimed. Reducing the color tax to the uncolored level, he argued, would conveniently bring the government more money for national defense. As an unheeding Senate voted down his eloquent move, Underwood blamed "the Creamery Trust"—which "desired the oleomargarine situation to remain as it was . . . to get more exhorbitant prices"—an opinion that was widely shared.[34]

Within a couple of months America entered World War I. The first great wartime fats shortage and a sharp rise in the cost of living greatly increased the demand for the spread well into 1920. In 1920 consumption attained a peak of 370 million pounds, or 3.5 pounds average per person.

Confronted with a shortage of fats, manufacturers turned full-scale to imported coconut oil, considered excellent for the purpose. By 1920 it contributed 45 per cent of the fats that went into margarine. A vegetable-animal fat blend type of margarine had come into wide use. Consumer familiarity had been enhanced. The old problem of dealer fraud substantially ended.[35] By 1920 there were 78 plants—an all-time high.

Postwar adjustment brought consumption down to 191 million pounds by 1922. Though margarine was not to partake fully in the expansion of the twenties, some solid sales growth did take place so that per capita use in 1930 showed 2.6 pounds and production 326 million pounds. The number of plants went down and then up; in 1930 there were 68. Margarine began to assume greater importance as a food in the South and on the West Coast.

An association of its manufacturers, organized in 1920, bannered the idea that "It behooves us . . . to stop talking margarine as a substitute and sell it on its own merits." To "give the American people complete information about our product" became the manufacturers' aim.[36] Charged with this mission was Dr. J. S. Abbott, a respected chemist and former food regulatory official. Important support came from leaders in science and education.

The housewife began to be offered a wider choice of margarine formulas. She also saw the price go down from the postwar high to an average of 31 cents in 1922, then to 25 cents in 1930. Butter's cost dropped less so that by 1930 the dime tax clearly failed to bridge the difference. Margarine in the nineteen-twenties was in a position to win more customers and its advertising began to be more of a factor than previously.

A pamphlet issued by Abbott in 1927 on composition and food value received extensive circulation. Another cited an impressive list of testimonials. Professor W. O. Hedrick of Michigan Agricultural College gave his opinion in 1924 that margarine offered "a product of a most satisfactory sort." Others were more emphatic, but Hedrick was daring the tolerance of his dairy state's legislature.[37]

The educational job was all uphill. Though influential men such as Wiley might berate the tax as "a violation of ethics and fair competition"[38] the restrictionist forces had grown more formidable. Armored with better organization, spurred by the postwar farm depression and allied with a solid farm bloc in Congress, they poured out publicity against "oleo." They pictured the use of coconut oil as the "coconut cow," a symbol of low-cost imported tropical fat that, they asserted, threatened every American farm. The manufacturers' organization appealed for some compromise, but the response was negative and unqualified. "What we need is drastic action," said one dairy spokesman, calling for "laws in every state." Cottonseed interests fought back at dairymen with threats of reprisal.[39]

Continuing attempts in Congress to lighten or strengthen the federal restrictions all wound up in stalemate. In 1924, however, Oregon and Washington voters turned down virtually prohibitive laws barring the use of milk in margarine. In California two years later voters rejected a two cent tax. The Federal Trade Commission stepped in to stop local boycotts against margarine. Wisconsin's Supreme Court in 1926 upheld a lower court decision that found margarine to be a healthful food and threw out a law barring use of milk in it. Only in Utah did a legislature enact a tax, in 1929 (and as late as 1970 refused to repeal it).[40]

However, when, in late 1930, the government decided that a margarine colored by containing ten per cent or more of dark palm oil was free from the tax,[41] angry rural Congressmen secured a new amendment to the 1902 law that placed the 10 cents tax on naturally as well as artificially colored margarine.[42]

The press was critical. One Midwestern editor found himself "wishing . . . that the organized dairymen would find a way to prosper that is not at the expense of the poor." Another demanded that "anti-oleomargarine racketeering really should be held in restraint." Margarine was seen by another observer "to reflect not something of evil but rather something of good." Southern cottonseed spokesmen portrayed their section as an injured partner in the national economy.[43]

Nevertheless the depression fostered many state taxes aimed to equalize oleomargarine and butter prices. Some 136 bills were counted in 30 states in 1931; in eight states taxes were imposed, usually from a nickel on white margarine to ten or twenty cents on colored. A number of southern states taxed margarine made of foreign fats. There was more southern grumbling at northern laws that failed to recognize cottonseed oil in margarine.[44]

Consumption reacted, dropping to 1.6 pounds per person national average in 1932.[45] While one food editor extolled margarine in 1932 as a food that could "scarcely be called a substitute any longer,"[46] the year 1936 was high noon for the restrictive system. Besides the federal taxes and licenses, 27 states prohibited colored margarine's manufacture or sale, 24 imposed some kind of consumer tax, and 26 imposed licenses or other restrictions.[47] The Army, Navy, and certain federal agencies were barred from its use except for cooking purposes. Even the tariffs on margarine and butter in 1930 and on coconut oil in 1934 were sharply increased.

Thus hemmed in, some sought in Congress an exemption for

domestic-fat margarine from the color tax. But by 1938 this proposal had achieved nothing but friction within the farm bloc.

BREAKTHROUGH, 1938-1950

Even during the adversities of the nineteen-thirties the tide slowly began to turn. Consumption regained lost ground and by 1942 had reached a new high aided by lower retail prices. Margarine packaging improved; and its advertising by 1940 had acquired more effectiveness. Spurred by competition, better margarines appeared, their manufacture aided by the new closed-system Votator production process.

Discoveries relating to the refining of cottonseed and other oils contributed to better formulas. Manufacturers devised all-vegetable margarines composed of cottonseed oil and later of blends of this and soybean oil. Between 1930 and 1943 margarine was transformed into a market for 500 instead of 100 million pounds of home-raised fats and oils. The share of vegetable oils in margarine manufacture had gone up from 76 to 95 per cent, of which cottonseed oil secured half.

This major shift in composition helped keep margarine's retail cost low—the average was 20 cents in 1931 and 17 cents in 1941. The consumer began to realize more money savings by buying margarine instead of butter. Pre-colored margarine began to appear in more stores.

Margarine had had to be defended against the charge that its comparative lack of vitamin A impaired its value in the diet to a meaningful extent.[48] During the nineteen-thirties, however, vitamin A fortification of margarine began to be general and some products were also fortified with vitamin D. The establishment of a Federal Standard in 1941 recognized margarine as a nutritious spread of its own kind.[49]

Early in the "New Deal," Secretary of Agriculture Henry A. Wallace had warned that "no degree of agitation against butter substitutes" would check their progress.[50] The changeover to domestic fats helped popularize this view. The margarine political struggle was taken up by the new National Cotton Coun-

cil and soybean associations. These interests began to speak out
with increasing effect. Food retailers joined in.[51] Support came
from those who were fighting laws in restraint of trade.[52]

Consumer consciousness had grown during the depression and
was just beginning to find voice in government—highlighted by
a National Nutrition Conference in 1941 where agricultural
experts spoke up for margarine as a desirable farm product re-
flecting more efficient use of land resources.[53]

Millions of Americans first turned to margarine during World
War II. They discovered they were required to do the coloring
themselves if they wished to avoid the tax. They were encouraged by a ration point system intended to divert consumption to margarine so that more milk would go into whole-
milk products. Margarine's consumer cost during the war stayed
around 24 cents a pound.

Efforts to remove margarine restrictions intensified. In 1943
Oklahoma broke through with the first of a long string of
significant state repeal actions. By 1947 legislative or court
actions had removed color or other barriers in several states.
Congressional interest in removing the federal taxes flared up in
1943 and 1944 when consumers joined oilseed and livestock
farm producers to present their case. Hand-coloring margarine
was "ridiculous," one consumer representative told a committee;
besides, Congress had increased the cost of pre-coloring "by a
minimum of 12½ cents to everybody who uses it."[54]

Yet the legislative situation might not have significantly
changed for years had not a crisis in dairy production costs
occurred in 1947. In December butter reached a dollar a pound.
Repeal bills in Congress suddenly multiplied. Early in 1948 an
all-out onslaught on the federal law exploded in Congress and
in editorial pages throughout the country.

The controversy—a topic of national interest—dragged out
over more than two years. It rapidly became complicated in
the number of issues raised, voluminous in the arguments presented, and insistent for action. Innumerable moves and delays
encumbered progress for Congress was hesitant and the dairy
opposition was adamant. Hundreds of thousands of letters

were received by members of Congress. Four major hearings took place. They were repetitive but they encompassed the length and breadth of the margarine issue. The full story of the margarine tax fight in Congress would be a history in itself.

The narrative of events may be condensed into principal turning points. A highly publicized hearing concluded with a refusal of a majority of the House Agriculture Committee to take any action. At this juncture a champion appeared in the person of Representative L. Mendel Rivers of South Carolina. For sessions past he had persistently presented bills to take off the taxes and had been ignored. He had done so in 1947 and now persuaded legislators to sign a petition for his bill's release from the imprisoning committee. This spectacular ploy succeeded on April 1, 1948. On April 28 the House passed the Rivers bill by a generous margin of 260 to 106 after a two-day struggle of unusual intensity.[55]

The Senate held back. Many of its members from states with dairying wished to be shown that they could safely vote for tax-free colored margarine. As a result the Rivers measure was killed by inaction.

The issue was taken up at once when the new Congress convened in early 1949. The House farm committee again resisted. It reported out a proposal of dairy spokesmen that colored margarine be permitted to sell tax-free but only in intrastate commerce—which would have indirectly increased the product's cost to consumers. During the floor debate Representative W. R. Poage offered a straight repeal measure as an amendment. Two days of heated debate produced a vote for the Poage proposal by the narrow margin of twelve votes. This theatrical vote was the crucial turning point in the fight to free margarine.

Eventually, after amendment, the Senate passed the House tax repeal measure. The Margarine Act of 1950 was signed by President Truman on March 23, 1950. On July 1 the federal margarine tax system came to an end.[56]

Since 1950

The results of the Act of 1950 were not long in coming. Margarine consumption increased dramatically although not as much as some had predicted. Consumption in 1950 was about 937 million pounds; by ~~1940~~ *1960* it had risen to nearly 1,700 million— an average gain of some 8 per cent a year national average— and in 1969 it reached 2,141 million. Per person use had risen from 6 to nearly 11 pounds.[57] Consumers indeed have used the tax-free margarine made available by repeal.

The two principal objectives of the federal act were quickly realized—pre-coloring and the saving of the tax and related cost. Margarine colored yellow soon became the predominant type, uncolored margarine being restricted to the two states still keeping their restrictions on the colored product or to certain industrial types. Store availability became almost universal. New margarine manufacturers entered the industry through the establishment of plants or acquisition of existing facilities.

The average price reported for colored margarine, untaxed, for 1950 was 31 cents a pound. Reported prices from then on indicated that the tax amount had been passed on to consumers. Released from restrictions, the retail price became more subject to competitive pressure and proceeded downwards. It averaged 29½ cents for the period 1951-1969.[58]

The expansion of margarine availability to stores brought about a new competitive situation. Lower-priced and premium margarines grew. Innovation became a mainspring. No longer required to be sold from shipping containers, margarines could utilize refrigerated displays to better advantage. The market developed specialized sectors. About 1956 there appeared the first of a series of special-feature margarines.[59] Repeal had enlarged consumer choices and encouraged competition.

The margarine market for home fats and oils realized the hopes of its proponents. Consumption of fats increased almost yearly and totaled 1,744 million pounds in 1969, practically all American-produced. Cottonseed oil relinquished its place to soybean oil as a result of the effect of price support on the former's cost. After 1960 corn and safflower and other oils became significant. Agriculture made newer fat ingredients available to margarine and produced more milkfat for non-butter uses.[60]

State prohibitions of colored margarine and other state restrictive laws began to go off the statute books, but not without severe struggles. In important states such as Illinois, Ohio, Pennsylvania, and New York the protectionist system against margarine collapsed only under sustained effort.[61] Minnesota in 1963 and Wisconsin in 1967 completed nationalization of colored margarine by removing their bans on it. By 1970 the principal legal restrictions remaining were per pound excise taxes in five states, two of which were scheduled to expire. Legislatures found it difficult to let go of these consumer taxes as margarine sales increased and the taxes provided revenue. On the federal scene some of the old restrictionism remained.

By 1970 margarine's new era had finished a first stage. Post-repeal expansion had slowed down. The spread had become a generally accepted food product and, as the preceeding sections have described, had changed in significant ways—in its products, composition, distribution and legal status. It had reflected the fast-moving changes in the American food market and the shifting patterns of food consumption and preference. As the first hundred years since the invention of oleomargarine drew to a close, margarine had become the leader in its part of the national diet and had demonstrated that this form of food was capable of providing new consumer tastes and conveniences. Its future will be one of marketing and product experimentation.

1. Conversation with writer, August 18, 1964.

2. The major references are Katharine Snodgrass, *Margarine as a Butter Substitute* (Stanford, 1930), and Martha C. Howard, "The Margarine Industry in the United States" (Ms., Columbia University, 1951). These contain useful bibliographies. There are a number of collateral treatises on one phase or another.

3. U. S. Patent Office No. 146,012. Re-issue to Mège were Nos. 5,868, May 12, 1874, and 8,424, September 24, 1878. He applied for another re-issue but seemingly his death on May 31, 1880, intervened. In all the materials found on Mège-Mouriés, no other connection between him and the United States occurs.

4. "Mège-Mouriés, der Erfinder von Margarin," ms. For this and other documentary material on Mège-Mouriéz the writer is indebted to Mr. A. Braakman, Unilever, N.V., Rotterdam. It is referred to hereinafter as the Unilever Archive. Also, Maurice Bouvat, *La Découverte de la Margarine par Mège-Mouriés* (n.p. n.d.).

5. Alex Berman, "Conflict and Anomaly in the Scientific Orientation of French Pharmacy, 1800-1873," in *Bulletin of the History of Medicine*, XXXVII, 440-62 (September-October 1963); Maurice Bouvat, "Mege-Mouries," in *Revue D'Histoire de la Pharmacie*, 82-88 (December 1946).

6. Thomas J. Thackeray, *Military Organization and Administration of France* (London, 1856) does not list butter or other fats in the French army ration. A sidelight on the meager role of butter is given by J. C. Drummond, *The Englishman's Food* (London, 1958), 281 ff. and Charles Wilson, *History of Unilever* (London, 1954), II,. 24.

7. Dr. J. Alphen, "From Chevreul to Mège-Mouriés," ms. For this report and other materials the writer is indebted to Unilever, N.V. and to the International Federation of Margarine Associations.

8. The invention history is more fully described through the documents in the Unilever Archive and in various secondary accounts. Among the latter are Snodgrass, *Margarine*, ch. XI; Wilson, *History of Unilever*, II, 25; P. N. Williams, *Margarine* (New York, 1965), 1 ff.; J. Fritsch, *Fabrication de la Margarine et des Graisses Alimentaires* (Paris, 1905), 17-19; M. K. Schwitzer, *Margarine* (London, 1956), ch. II.

9. Timmothée Trimm (pseud., Napoleon Lespes), *Le Beurre Frais Pour Tous* (Paris, 1874); *Moniteur Scientifique-Quesneville*, Livr. 369e, 741-44 (September 1872).

10. Wilson, *History of Unilever*, 28-29; Williams, *Margarine*, 3-4; W. Schutaf, *Die Margarine in Deutschland und in der Welt* (Hamburg, 1942).

11. Henry C. Mott, Jr., "Manufacture of Artificial Butter," in *American Chemist*, VII, 233-35 (December 1876) also his *Complete History and Process of the Manufacture of Artificial Butter* (New York, 2nd ed., 1876); *Nature*, XV (1882), 269-70. The crediting of the first oleomargarine produced in the United States to makers of culinary fats, prior to the United States Dairy Company, may be a confusion of "oleomargarine" and "oleomargarine oil."

12. Quoted in *Dairy Foods Review*, LVIII, 8 (December 1953).

13. *Scientific American*, XLII, 259 (April 28, 1880); Howard, *Margarine Industry*, 11, 12-15, 24.

14. Howard, *Margarine Industry*, 65 ff.; 92; William Clayton, *Margarine* (New York, 1920), 210; H. C. Alvord, "Dairy Development in the United States," in *Yearbook of Agriculture, 1899* (Washington, 1890), 401; Jelke ms. in Chicago Historical Society.

15. O. E. Anderson, *Health of a Nation* (Chicago, 1958), 136; H. W. Wiley to J. D. Mickle, September 3, 1927, in files of National Association of Margarine Manufacturers; A. Dewees, *State and Federal Legislation and Decisions Relating to Margarine* (Washington, 1936), 15; *Speeches of Hon. Oscar W. Underwood . . . 1917* (Washington, 1917), 46, 49.

16. U. S. Senate, Committee on Agriculture, *Hearings on S. 1837* . . . .

(Washington, 1886), 1 ff.; J. T. Schlebecker, "Dairy Journalism," in *Agricultural History*, XXXI, 40 (October 1957).

17. S. L. Clemens (Mark Twain), *Life on the Mississippi* (New York, 1911), 304-5.

18. *Report of the Commissioner of Agriculture for the Year 1879* (Washington, 1880), 77; U. S. Department of Agriculture, Division of Chemistry, *Bulletin 13* (Washington, 1887), 19. One manufacturer's response was to create a better quality product. "Jelke Influence on the Margarine Industry," ms. in Chicago   Historical Society.

19. Howard, *Margarine Industry*, 36; also 69, 63-73.

20. *People vs. Marx*, 99 New York 177 (1885).

21. James D. Richardson, *Messages and Papers of the Presidents*, (n.p., 1898), VIII, 407. The Act of 1886 is: Ch. 840, 24 Stat. 209.

22. H. C. Bonnard, "The Oleomargarine Law," in *Political Science Quarterly*, II, 545-55 (December 1887); Howard, *Margarine Industry*, 40.

23. *Powell vs. Pennsylvania*, 127 U. S. 678 (1888) and *Shollenberger vs. Pennsylvania*, 171 U. S. 1 (1898) were the state law decisions. *In re Kollock*, 165 U.S. 526 (1896) upheld the 1886 Act; see also W. L. King, *Melville W. Fuller* (Chicago, 1876 ed.), 238-39. For the impact of the "original package" doctrine and the Wilson Act of 1890, see Snodgrass, *Margarine*, 48-49.

24. U. S. Congress, 71st Congress, 1st Session, House of Representatives, *Hearings . . . on H.R. 15934* (Washington, 1931), 194; *Id.*, 57th Congress, 1st Session, Senate Committee on Agriculture and Forestry, *Hearings . . . on H.R. 9206* (Washington, 1902), 101. It was stated that the oleomargarine coloring material, the vegetable product annatto, had been adopted for coloring butter also (Washington *Times*, February 17, 1912) but both products exchanged technical ideas freely (Anderson, *Margarine*, 79 ff.).

25. *Plumley v. Massachusetts*, 155 U. S. 461 (1894); *Collins v. New Hampshire*, 171 U. S. 30 (1898).

26. 21 U.S.C.A., Sec. 2301, upheld by the Supreme Court in *McCrary v. U. S.*, 195 U. S. 27 (1904). The second act is: 21 U.S.C.A. 25.

27. U. S. Congress, 57th Congress, 1st Session, *Senate Report No. 530, Part I* (Washington 1902), 5.

28. Springfield, Missouri, *Leader*, February 10, 1912; Nashville *Banner*, February 2, 1912.

29. A list of manufacturers with historial annotations is in Appendix C. Practically no individual firm records of pre-1940 have survived.

30. U. S. Congress, House of Representatives, 62nd Congress, 3rd Session, *House Report No. 1572* (Washington, 1913), 1.

31. Burlington, Iowa, *Hawkeye*, and Lewiston, Maine, *Sun*, February 9, 1912; Chicago *Record-Herald*, February 16, 1912; Marquette, Michigan, *Daily Journal*, February 7, 1912; A. L. Carlsbad, *Health Through National Diet* (Philadelphia, 1912), 191-92; Scrapbooks of clippings, 1911-12, National Association of Margarine Manufacturers.

32. U. C. Commissioner of Internal Revenue, *Annual Report, 1911* (Washington, 1911), 19. See also Chicago *Inter-Ocean*, February 26, 1912.

33. These proposals established a further precedent in their deliberate choice

of the name "margarine." See N. Y. *Journal of Commerce,* February 26, 1912. At least one writer thought "oleomargarine" a handicap name; Springfield, Massachusetts, *Republican,* February 23, 1912. The name margarine would have been legalized by a proposal for tax relief in Congress in 1920. *Butter, Cheese and Egg Journal,* April 28, 1920.

34. *Speeches of Hon. Oscar W. Underwood . . . .* (Washington, 1917), 5 30-33, 55 *et passim;* Rhinelander, Wisconsin, *News,* February 23, 1912.

35. Snodgrass, *Margarine,* Chapter VIII.

36. *Proceedings of the Second Annual Convention of the Institute of Margarine Manufacturers, 1921* (Washington, 1921), 39; Howard, *Margarine Industry,* 205.

An early effort was by the National Association of Margarine Manufacturers, *The Importance of the Margarine Industry to American Agriculture* (Washington, 1921). Abbott during his long service wrote hundreds of articles and delivered a large number of speeches. Among the pamphlets issued by the manufacturers' group between 1929 and 1935, all at Washington, these were significant: *Composition and Food Value of Margarine* (1927); *Opinions of Educators and Statesmen on Margarine . . . .* (1925); *Turning on the Light: The True Story of Margarine* (n.d.); *Questions and Answers about Margarine* (n.d.). J. S. Abbott, margarine publicity scrapbook and other mss., files of the National Association of Margarine Manufacturers.

37. *Opinions of Educators . . . on Margarine,* 10.

38. H. W. Wiley to J. D. Mickle, September 3, 1927, in files of National Association of Margarine Manufacturers; see also his letter to G. B. Thompson in New Orleans *Item,* February 16, 1912, and comment in New Orleans *Picayune,* February 25, 1912.

39. *Dairy Farmer,* XLVIII, 8 (March 1, 1925) quoted in Howard, *Margarine Industry,* Chapter III. The southern cottonseed-margarine movement is reflected in Baton Rouge *Press,* and Asheville *Citizen,* February 20; Texarkana *Texarkanian,* February 27; Charlotte *Observer,* March 3; and Houston *Chronicle,* March 8, 1925. The anti-margarine effort is reflected in *Hoard's Dairyman,* April 2, 1920, and *Dairyman's League,* December 28, 1923, and other press clippings in mss. scrapbook, files of the National Association of Margarine Manufacturers.

40. Clippings and letters, files of the National Association of Margarine Manufacturers. The *National Provisioner,* February 13, 1926, discussed the important Wisconsin decision, *John F. Jelke et al. vs. Emery,* 193 Wisconsin 311 (January 18, 1926). The main Congressional struggle is reported in *Journal of Oil and Fat Industries,* March, 1926.

41. The subject is covered in more detail by Snodgrass, *Margarine,* Chapter VI, and Howard, *Margarine Industry,* Chapter III.

42. Act of March 4, 1931, Chapter 520, 46 Stat. 1549, 26 U.S.C. No. 2300 (Internal Revenue Code of 1854, No. 4592). In 1930, another enactment had revised the definition of oleomargarine, among other things to include vegetable oils.

43. Decatur, Illinois, *Herald,* March 18, 1931; Cedar Falls, Iowa, *Record,* November 17, 1931; *Is There Any Jusification . . . Address of the Hon. Ellison*

D. Smith . . . March 2, 1931 (n.p., n.d.); Omaha *Evening World-Herald,*
April 8, 1931; Denver *Daily Record Stockman,* April 14, 1931; W. R. Pabst,
Jr., *Butter and Oleomargarine* (N. Y. 1937), 84. A leading dairy journal re-
flected the idea that margarine had caused lower butter use and prices
(*Hoard's Dairyman,* February 10, 1930).

44. National Association of Margarine Manufacturers, *An Appeal to Reason*
(Columbus, 1936); U. S. Department of Agriculture, *State and Federal Legislation and Decisions Relating to Oleomargarine* (Washington, 1936). For the
domestic-fats taxes movement, see Howard, *Margarine Industry,* 195-96, 280
ff.

45. On the effects of the laws, see Pabst, *Butter and Margarine,* Chapter
III; G. W. Ladd, "Trends in Margarine Legislation," in *Journal of Marketing,*
XXIV, 65-69 (April, 1960); Howard, *Margarine Industry,* 339 *et seq.*

46. Chicago *Tribune,* March 17, 1932.

47. National Association of Margarine Manufacturers, *An Appeal to Reason*
(Columbus, 1936), 21; *id., The Story of Margarine* (Columbus, c. 1937); In-
stitute of Margarine Manufacturers, "Editorial and Individual Comment on
Margarine Tax Legislation" (Washington, 1932).

48. For example, NAMM, *Composition and Food Value of Margarine;* W.
H. Eddy, "What Is Margarine Good For?" in Good Housekeeping, LXXXVIII,
97, 250-52 (April, 1929); D. Waters, "The Truth About Margarine," in *The
Woman* (June 1945); Richardson, *Vitamines Doctrine.*

49. See Chapter V on the nutritional history of margarine.

50. Speech at Syracuse, N. Y., September 5, 1933, quoted in Jansen, *Appeal
to Reason,* 30; see also "Letter to Congressman Wadsworth . . . April 2,
1936" (mimeographed copy, files of National Association of Margarine Manufacturers); Howard, *Margarine Industry,* 309.

51. Some examples are: National Cottonseed Products Association, *A
Southern Product Seeks Its Market* (Memphis, n.d.); *Cotton and Cotton Oil
Press,* September 26, 1936, 14; October 11, 1941, 5; April 11, 1942, 12; August
29, 1942, 10; E. S. Haines, *United The South and The West.* . . . (Memphis,
1933); National Cotton Council of America, *By What Right?* (Memphis,
1940); T. H. Whitehead, *Margarine and Georgia* (Athens, 1940); G. M.
Strayer, *An Outlet for Soybean Oil* (Hudson, Iowa, 1940); U. S. Congress,
Senate, *Hearings Before a Subcommittee of the Agriculture and Forestry* . . .
on S. 1744 (Washington, 1944), 103-106. A typical approach is J. S. Abbott,
"Domestic Fats and Oils" (mimeographed, April 12, 1937). For retailers, see
National Association of Retail Grocers, *Why Congress Should Repeal* . . .
(Chicago, n.d.). A sizeable literature of argument between oilseed and dairy
organizations on the margarine issue accumulated by 1950, as this agricultural
schism continued to expand. See also Wesley McCune, *The Farm Bloc* (Garden
City, 1943), Chapter VII.

52. For example, U. S. Department of Agriculture, *Barriers to Internal Trade
In Farm Products* (Washington, 1939), 17-30; U. S. Department of Commerce,
Trade Barriers in the Food Industry (Washington, 1943), 29-40; Council of
State Governments, *Margarine Excise Taxes as Trade Barriers* (Chicago,
(1939); W. R. Pabst, Jr., "Interstate Trade Barriers and State Oleomargarine

Taxes," in *Southern Economic Journal,* VII, 505-517 (April, 1941).

53. For example, in the nutrition area: J. S. Abbott, "Place of Margarine in Nutrition and Health Movements" (ms. in files of National Association of Margarine Manufacturers). In the farm area see: O. H. Brownlee, *Putting Dairying on a War Footing* (Ames, Iowa, 1943)—a report which occasioned an uproar and the departures of faculty members from the then Iowa State College.

54. U. S. Congress, 78th Congress, 1st Session, House of Representatives, *Hearings Before the Committee on Agriculture . . . on H. R. 2400* (Washington, 1943), 278, *et passim; id.,* Senate, *Hearings Before the Committee on Finance . . . on H. R. 3687* (Washington, 1943), 339-56; *id.,* 2nd Session, Senate, *Hearings Before a Subcommittee of the Committee on Agriculture . . . on S. 1744* (Washington, 1944; McCune, *Farm Bloc,* 108-112, 11; *Fortune,* XXIX, 132 ff. (November, 1943).

55. *Congressional Record,* 80th Congress, 2nd Session, 5130 (April 28, 1948).

56. *Ibid.,* 81st Congress, 1st Session, 3732 (April 1, 1949). The March 16, 1950, Margarine Act (Chapter 61, 64 Stat. 20, 21 U.S.C. §347a (1954)), removed all the taxes and licenses and fees. It required colored margarine to be sold retail in weights of not over one pound. Colored margarine in public eating places was subject to notification requirements which, later, were issued by the Food and Drug Administration. Dairy terms in advertising were prohibited, by an amendment to the Federal Trade Commission Act. Most of the new or amended state laws since 1950 have carried the same public eating place requirement. Space does not permit illustrative quotations from the plentiful press and debate sources. Arguments are summed up in U. S. Senate, Committee on Finance, *Issues of Oleomargarine Tax Repeal* (Washington, committee print, 1948).

57. Production and consumption figures are in the Appendices, Tables I and III.

58. Margarine price figures are given in the Appendices, Table II.

59. See Chapters I and III.

60. Ingredients utilized in margarine are reviewed in Chapter II. See also Chapter IV for a fuller discussion of margarine and agriculture.

61. The appearance of various types of "imitation" dairy products has directed attention to the old margarine laws as a course of action proved to be unsuccessful. For example, E. B. Weiss, "Dairies May be Repeating Oleo Mistake," in *Advertising Age,* XXXIX, 73-74 (February 19, 1968).

LEGAL CITATIONS: STATUTES, REGULATIONS AND DECISIONS

FEDERAL STATUTES

Act of March 16, 1950 (Federal Margarine Act), 64 Stat. 20, 21 U.S.C., § 347.

Act of August 2, 1886 (Oleomargarine Act), ch. 840, 24 Stat. 209 as amended; ch. 784, 82 Stat. 193 (1902), as amended; ch. 882, 46 Stat. 1022 (1930), as amended; ch. 520, 46 Stat. 1549 (1931).

Fair Packaging and Labeling Act, 80 Stat. 1296 (1966), 15 U.S.C., § 1451.

Federal Food, Drug, and Cosmetic Act, 52 Stat. 1040 (1938), as amended 21 U.S.C., § 301.

Federal Trade Commission Act, 38 Stat. 717 (1914), as amended, 15 U.S.C., § 41.

Internal Revenue Code of 1954, § 4591 (margarine import tax).

Navy Ration Statute of 1933, 10 U.S.C., § 6982.

Wholesome Meat Act, 81 Stat. 584 (1967), 21 U.S.C., § 601.

FEDERAL REGULATIONS

Food and Drug Administration Regulations, Title 21 Code of Federal Regulations—

§ 1.1c(a) Exemptions from required label statements (for margarine under the Fair Packaging and Labeling Act).

§ 3.17 Labeling of oleomargarine or margarine.

§ 3.41 Status of articles offered to the general public for the control or reduction of blood cholesterol levels and for the prevention and treatment of heart and artery disease under the Federal Food, Drug, and Cosmetic Act. (Under review, 1970).

§ 45.1 Oleomargarine, margarine; identity; label statement of optional ingredients.

§ 45.2 Liquid oleomargarine, liquid margarine; identity label statement of optional ingredients.

U.S. Department of Agriculture Meat Inspection Regulations, Title 9 Code of Federal Regulations—

§ 317.8 (c) (25) False or deceptive labeling practices.

§ 318.6 (a) (2) (Margarine) processes to be supervised; containers, equipment, processes of manufacture to be clean and sanitary; substances to be clean and wholesome.

§ 328.1 Oleomargarine or margarine; identity; label statement of optional ingredients.

COURT CASES

Collins v. New Hampshire, 171 U.S. 20 (1898).

Coy v. Linder, 18 Ga. 583, 189 S.E. 26 (1936).

E. F. Drew & Co., Inc. v. F.T.C., 235 F.2d 735 (2d Cir. 1956).

Higgins Mfg. Co. v. Page, 297 Fed. 644 (D.R.I. 1924).

In re Kollock, 165 U.S. 526 (1897).

J. F. Jelke Co. v. Emery, 193 Wis. 311, 214 N.W. 369 (1927).

Land O'Lakes Creameries, Inc. v. McNutt, 132 F.2d 658 (8th Cir. 1943).

Magnano Co. v. Hamilton, 292 U.S. 40 (1924).

McCray v. United State, 195 U.S. 27 (1904).

People v. Marx, 99 N.Y. 377, 2 N.E. 29 (1885).

Plumley v. Massachusetts, 155 U.S. 461 (1894).

Powell v. Pennsylvania, 127 U.S. 678 (1888).

Reddi-Spred Corp. v. F.T.C., 229 F.2d 557 (3rd Cir. 1956).

Schollenberger v. Pennsylvania, 171 U.S. 1 (1898).

Schmitt v. Nord, 71 S.D. 575 27 N.W. 2d 910 (1934).

Thorin v. Burke, 146 Neb. 94, 18 N.W. 2d 66 (1945).

U.S. v. 856 Cases . . . "Demi," etc., Civil No. 10186, N.D.N.Y., April 22, 1966 (memorandum).

WORLD MARGARINE PRODUCTION

The data supplied below are largely based on the reported figures provided by the sources cited. Trade information, however, also has been employed. It is not possible to have a firm figure on production in some nations where reporting is not complete.

The profile appears to be generally correct nevertheless. It shows that in 1969 margarine production world-wide reached well over ten billion pounds. This total includes vanaspati, a vegetable ghee made and consumed in India and Pakistan, which is a substitute for traditional ghee (a buffalo milk fat product clarified to remove moisture and containing 99 percent fat).

The United States is the single largest national producer of margarine, contributing in 1969 roughly a fifth or more of world production. Western Europe, the historic home of margarine, is the major manufacturing and consumption area, contributing about a third. Nearly two-thirds of this is in the European Economic Community which includes some of the leading margarine producing countries — West Germany and the Netherlands to name the leaders. Recently, the U.S.S.R. appears to be increasing its production of margarine and to have taken second place after the United States in volume.

Since World War II margarine or comparable food products have appeared and grown in regions where they had not before had any significant place, notably Israel, Egypt, and Japan. Margarine is made in Turkey, Thailand, and Tanzania. In its newer homes the food tends to be used as a cooking ingredient. In Australia, Canada, and South Africa, margarine is well established but continues to be limited in consumption because of restrictive laws and quotas. In sum, the world-wide margarine picture is a diverse one. It is a cosmopolitan food with considerable adaptability to national preferences of taste and composition.

In the western countries the consumption of margarine is

more or less influenced by the supplies available and prices of butter. This is particularly true in many of the major margarine-producing nations. Butter production world-wide in 1968 and 1969 is reported to have been 10,753 and 10,447 million pounds, respectively.[1] In 1969 the European Economic Community faced a serious problem of butter surpluses owing to policies of aid to dairy producers that resulted in over-production of milk and milkfat. This has affected world markets for the dairy spread. It has also had some effect on margarine consumption overall.

Margarine does not enter largely into international trade. American imports and exports are practically nil. Within western Europe there is some trade in margarine and also from western Europe and the United Kingdom to certain importing places such as Cyprus and Ghana. Total world exports in 1969 are estimated to have been about 80 million pounds. More basic is the international trade in the fats and oils ingredients of margarines made in western Europe and other countries that must import much of their margarine ingredient supplies.

An important distinction between United States and world (especially European) margarine consumption lies in the absence or limited volume of shortening consumption overseas. Shortening and cooking compounds in 1969 were consumed here at the national average rate of about 17 pounds per capita. While such products have made an appearance in some European countries, the shortening role is performed to a great extent by margarine. Much margarine is produced for this purpose alone, and the trade distinction between "table" and "cooking" or industrial margarine is more important there than here.

Another difference is that of food habits. Butter retains favor in some countries—French cookery emphasizes it; however, the Danes and Dutch produce butter largely for export and themselves often use margarine. Also some regions, such as southern France, Italy and Spain, retain a traditional liking for olive and other liquid oils. In the Near East margarine or margarine-like fats serve as cooking fats as well as for use with breads.

The world margarine consumption picture varies by nations. In general, it is one of long range growth.[2] World production since World War II has gone well ahead of that of previous times. During the period 1962-68 it advanced at an average rate of three percent annually, while butter increased about two percent. Population in the principal margarine-butter utilizing countries has been going up about one percent a year, but world population has been growing at a rate closer to two percent.

Much of margarine's recent expansion showing is because of the increase in the United States and Russia. As a basic type of food, however, it obviously figures in many proposals for combatting the mounting threat of world hunger — especially as developing countries turn more to protein-type foods which sometimes require a spread for palatability. About a sixth of the world's food fat comes from margarine; it is second only to butter in the ranking of solid food fats.

There are significant differences in the compositions of margarines in the United States as compared with those of Western Europe and elsewhere. The 80 percent fat minimum required here is not universally followed, although it is called for in a proposed international margarine standard under preparation by United Nations agencies. West Germany, for one example, requires 78 percent; Sweden, 82 percent; Spain and Switzerland, 84 percent.

The fat ingredients themselves are often different because of the dependence of many on importd supplies. Thus, coconut, palm kernel and palm oils are traditionally important in many European and other margarines. American soybean oil, the principal ingredient here by far, has made progress in European and Japanese margarines but has met severe competition from other supplies, such as sunflowerseed oil from the U.S.S.R.

The selection basis of fats and oils for margarine everywhere is founded on cost, though many premium margarines are prepared with formulas that call for more expensive oils. The spectrum of fats utilized is broader than in the United States and more subject to substitution of one fat or oil for another. For countries without large domestic supplies, this means that world fats and oils prices are directly linked to margarine ingredients selection.

Further, some countries mandate the use of specific fats and some the limited use of butter or milkfat. Thus, Sweden and West Germany often require the use of their domestic rapeseed oil in margarine under certain conditions relating to the domestic supply of rapeseed. Marine oils, frequently employed in Europe, are not used in American margarines.

World developments are involved: the rise of America's soybean agriculture, the diversion of tropical oils to the needs of local populations, the decline of whale fisheries, and the decisions of state-controlled agencies to enter markets for exchange or other purposes.

Other ingredients also may be subject to national laws or regulations, including the use of vitamins, colorings and flavorings, and identifying substances. As in the United States, margarine is a highly regulated food practically everywhere.

The amounts of the different fats and oils utilized in margarine by countries is reported by only a few governments.[*] A typical medium-priced European table margarine in 1967 was likely to contain one or more of the major fats utilized — coconut oil, palm oil, palm kernel oil, and marine oil. Peanut, sunflowerseed, rapeseed and other vegetable oils are also complementary ingredients. European margarines employ diverse formulas and come up with very good quality products.

Restricting margarine by law is an old and ubiquitous policy of many governments. Today it still takes many forms. In the United States most restrictive laws have been abandoned. In Europe there have been severe laws but, on the whole, the spirit has long been regulative rather than punitive or harrassing; exceptions are some prohibitions of colored margarine and recurrent proposals for some levy on margarine in favor of dairy butter.

All or nearly all countries with margarine production of any significance have special laws or regulations, or both, dealing with the product. A typical requirement is licensing of manufacturers; another, limitation of the place of retail sale and of the shape and weight of the retail package (in Europe, the usual "packet" is ¼ kilogram, wrapped in parchment) but other sizes may be found in some countries. A comprehensive statement by countries of many of the applicable laws and regulations has been prepared for its members by the International Federation of Margarine Associations, the world association of manufacturers.[*]

Retail prices of margarine naturally vary around the world. In Western Europe one rough guideline is that 20 to 25 cents American equivalent purchases the usual ¼ kilogram (a little over ½ pound) package. But retail prices vary a great deal between places and brands. United Kingdom margarine prices are often nearer butter prices than are those in the United States; on occasion, premium margarines have maintained sales at prices higher than those of butter.

Manufacturers' national trade organizations exist in each of the main producing countries of Europe and in Anstralia, Canada, Japan and (for vanaspati) in India. The International Federation of Margarine Associations, headquartered at the Hague, works through country associations. Among other accomplishments it has forwarded the development of an international Standard for margarine, an important project undertaken by the Food and Agricultural Organization and the World Health Organization, United Nations, as part of the world "Codex Alimentarius." The international Standard in 1970 was in the process of being referred to national governments for adoption, including the United States. It differs in certain particulars from the American Standards. Its eventual adoption would encourage good consumer Standards for margarine in many countries and possibly would improve the conditions of international trade in the product.

1. *Oilworld*, June 1970, p. 241.

2. An estimate prepared for the International Federation of Margarine Associations in 1967 was for world margarine production in 1975 in the developed regions (including Europe, United Kingdom, North America, Oceania) totaling from about 6,925 million to about 7,450 million pounds (Dr. Mirko Lamer, "Main Characteristics of Projections . . . Margarine" (Mimeo., International Federation of Margarine Associations, 1967), Table 5.

3. Some recent information is available in United Nations Food and Agriculture Organization, *Coconut Situation*, No. 22 (Rome, 1969); and the Commonwealth Secretariat publication *Vegetable Oils and Oilseeds*, No. 19 (London, 1970).

4. International Federation of Margarine Associations, *The Situation in the Margarine Industry* (1968). A tabulation appears in S. F. Riepma, *Margarine in Western Europe* (Washington, U. S. Department of Agriculture, 1959), p. 15.

MARGARINE PRODUCTION IN PRINCIPAL PRODUCING COUNTRIES

Area and Country	1968	1969
Western Europe and U. K.		
Austria	85.1	86.9
Belgium	288.0	289.7
Denmark	195.4	193.6
Finland	57.0	60.5
France	338.6	347.8
Western Germany	1,245.6	1,213.9
Irish Republic	n.a.	n.a.
Italy	99.0	101.2
Netherlands	569.6	531.7
Norway	184.8	184.6
Portugal	45.5	49.9
Spain	50.6	53.5
Sweden	274.5	281.8
Switzerland	n.a.	n.a.
United Kingdom	656.3	698.7
Eastern Europe and U.S.S.R.		
Czechoslovakia	108.2	110.0
East Germany	414.2	418.0
Hungary	n.a.	n.a.
Poland	303.6	321.2
Romania	n.a.	n.a.
U.S.S.R. (including compounds)	1,423.4	1,508.7
Yugoslavia	49.3	n.a.
North America		
Canada	194.0	202.6
United States	2,114.1	2,181.9
Central and South America	100[1]	100[1]
Other		
Australia	130.2	140.8
Egypt (butter substitute)	n.a.	n.a.
India (vanaspati)	1,042.8	1,071.4
Israel	49.5	51.5
Japan	195.6	226.6
Pakistan (vanaspati)	198.4	251.0
World Total[1]	10,894.4	11,179.2

1. Includes countries where no individual figures are available.

Sources: *Oilworld,* June 1970, p. 242; Food and Agriclltural Organization of the United Nations, *Coconut Situation,* No. 22 (Rome 1969). Comparative use has been made of Commonwealth Economic Committee, *Vegetable Oils and Oilseeds* (London 1970), p. 246, and of data from the International Federation of Margarine Associations, The U. S. Department of Agriculture, and trade sources.

Margarine is produced in some Central and South American countries, notably

Brazil, Columbia, Mexico and Venezuela. The gross output may be about 100 million pounds.

There is some variation between the figures found in different sources, and many of the figures appearing in the above table reflect some degree of compromise. The author acknowledges his indebtedness to Dr. J. Sevenster, Unilever N.V., and Mr. Harold V. Knight, consultant.

MARGARINE AND BUTTER CONSUMPTION PER CAPITA, SELECTED COUNTRIES (Pounds)

Country	1967		1968	
	Margarine	*Butter*	*Margarine*	*Butter*
Australia	10.6	21.9	11.0	21.6
Belgium	29.3	21.5	28.4	20.3
Canada	9.3	16.9	9.5	16.3
Denmark	39.8	21.7	39.7	20.7
Finland	10.5	37.5	12.1	35.0
France	6.5	19.6	6.8	19.8
Netherlands	43.2	7.3	43.0	3.9
New Zealand	......	42.4	......	40.5
Norway	47.7	8.8	43.2	13.0
Sweden	35.3	17.8	36.1	16.3
United Kingdom	11.7	19.5	11.2	19.6
United States	10.5	5.5	10.8	5.3
West Germany	21.0	18.7	20.7	18.5

Sources: *Die Agramärkte* (1969), p. 41; and private and trade sources.

LEADING MARGARINE MANUFACTURERS
IN THE UNITED STATES

ALLFRESH FOOD PRODUCTS, INC. General office and plant, 2156 Green Bay Road, Evanston, Illinois. Established in 1952, began manufacture the same year. Institutional and commercial margarines. Principal brands: Allfresh and Fold-N-Roll.

ANDERSON CLAYTON FOODS. General office, One Main Place, Dallas, Texas. Plants at Fresno, California; Jacksonville, Illinois; and Sherman, Texas. Entered manufacture in 1952. Consumer and industrial margarines. Principal house brands: Chiffon and Meadolake. Principal controlled brands: Golden Mist and Log Cabin.

ARMOUR & COMPANY. General office, 111 East Wacker Drive, Chicago, Illinois. Margarine manufacture is by Armour, Inc. and Collier & Son, Inc., an affiliated joint venture doing business as Collier Industries, with general office and plant at 815 Grove Street, Fort Worth, Texas. Established in 1897, the firm was one of the first American manufacturers of margarine, beginning in 1880; Collier Industries, since 1949. Consumer and industrial margarines. Principal house brands: Armour 99, Cloverbloom, and Mayflower.

BEST FOODS DIVISION, CPC INTERNATIONAL, INC. General office, Englewood Cliffs, New Jersey. Plants at Bayonne, New Jersey; Chicago, Dallas, and San Francisco. Best Foods Division originated in 1903 as the Nucoa Butter Company and began margarine manufacture in 1917. Consumer and industrial margarines. Principal house brands: Mazola and Nucoa.

BLUE PLATE FOODS, INC., Division of Hunt-Wesson Foods, Inc. General office and plant, 1315 South Jefferson Davis Parkway, New Orleans. Established on January 9, 1930, it went into margarine manufacturing in 1939. Consumer margarine. Principal house brand: Blue Plate.

CARTHAGE CREAMERY CO. General office and plant, 545 N. Main

Street, Carthage, Missouri. Established in 1917, it began margarine manufacture in 1951. Consumer margarine, specializing in private label. Principal house brand: Carmo.

COLLIER INDUSTRIES. See Armour & Company.

DREW CHEMICAL CORPORATION. General office, 522 Fifth Avenue, New York City. Plants at Boonton, New Jersey; and (through a subsidiary, Drew Foods Corporation) 3400 N. Wharf Street, St. Louis. Established in 1962, antecedent firm began manufacture in 1904. Consumer and industrial margarines. Principal house brand: Tri-Nut. Major controlled brand: Borden's New Danish.

GLIDDEN-DURKEE DIVISION, SCM CORPORATION. General office (Industrial Foods Division), 2333 Logan Boulevard, Chicago. Plant is at Chicago. Antecedent firm established in 1917 and began manufacture in 1918. Institutional and commercial margarines.

J. H. FILBERT, INC. General office, 3701 Southwestern Boulevard, Baltimore, Maryland. Plants are at Baltimore and at Macon, Georgia (temporary) and Atlanta, Georgia. Established in 1918. Consumer and industrial margarines. Principal house brand: Mrs. Filbert's.

GREGG'S FOOD PRODUCTS, INC. General office and plant, 9000 N. E. Marx Drive, Portland, Oregon. Established in 1946, the firm was incorporated in 1957; it began margarine manufacture in 1965. Consumer and industrial margarines. Principal house brands: Gregg's and Gold-n-Soft.

KENT PRODUCTS, INC. General office and plant, Wornall Road at 42nd Terrace, Kansas City, Missouri. Established in 1920, antecedent firm began margarine manufacture in 1911. Consumer and industrial margarines. Principal house brand: Richmade.

KRAFT FOODS, DIVISION OF KRAFTCO CORPORATION. General office, 500 Peshtigo Court, Chicago, Illinois. Plants are at Buena Park, California; Decatur, Georgia; Champaign, Illinois; Hillside, New Jersey; and Dallas, Texas. Established in 1903, it began margarine manufacture in 1937. Consumer proprietary brand margarines. Principal brands: Parkay, Kraft DeLuxe, Kraft Corn Oil, and Miracle (whipped).

LEVER BROTHERS COMPANY. General office, 390 Park Avenue, New York City. Plants are at Los Angeles, California; Hammond, Indiana; and Edgewater, New Jersey. Established in 1895, it began margarine manufacture in 1948. The parent company, Unilever, N.Y., acquired the first permanent margarine manufacturing operation in Europe, dating to 1878. Consumer and industrial margarines. Principal house brands: Imperial and Good Luck.

MADISON COOP CREAMERY. General office and plant, Madison, Nebraska. Established in 1920, it began margarine manufacture in 1967. Consumer margarine, proprietary and private label brands. Principal house brand: Lakeville Creameries.

MIAMI MARGARINE COMPANY. General office, 5226 Vine Street, Cincinnati, Ohio. Plants are at Cincinnati and Albert Lea, Minnesota. Established in 1918, the firm began margarine manufacture the same year. Consumer and industrial margarines. Principal house brand: Nu-Maid. Major specialty brand: Emdee.

OSCEOLA FOOD, INC. General office and plant, P. O. Box 368, Osceola, Arkansas. Established in 1948, it began margarine manufacture in 1949. Consumer and industrial margarines. Principal house brands: Farmbelle, Chief, and Margelo (liquid margarine).

SHEDD-BARTUSH FOODS, INC. General office, 14401 Dexter Boulevard, Detroit, Michigan. Plants are at Detroit and Sunnyvale, California; Elgin, Illinois; Omaha, Nebraska; Greenville, South Carolina; and Dallas, Texas. Antecedent firm began margarine manufacture in 1919. Consumer and industrial margarines. Principal house brands: Keyko, Churngold, Shedd's Safflower, Southern Gold, Sun Valley, Golden Corn, and Willow Run (all-vegetable).

STANDARD BRANDS, INC. General office, 625 Madison Ave., New York City. Plants at Atlanta, Dallas, Indianapolis, Oakland, and Pennsauken, N.J. Established in 1929, the firm began margarine manufacture in 1942 with the acquisition of Standard Margarine Co. Consumer and industrial margarines, all house brands. Principal brands: Blue Bonnet and Fleischmann's.

SUNNYLAND REFINING COMPANY. General office and plant, 3330

10th North, Birmingham, Alabama. Established in 1930, it began margarine manufacture in 1931. Consumer and industrial margarines. Principal house brand: Sunnyland.

SWIFT & COMPANY. General office, 115 West Jackson Boulevard, Chicago, Illinois. Plants are at Los Angeles, California; Kankakee, Illinois; Chattanooga, Tennessee; and Fort Worth, Texas. Established in 1855, it was one of the first manufacturers of margarine beginning about 1880. Consumer and industrial margarines. Principal house brands: Allsweet and Sundrop (liquid margarine). Principal controlled brands: First Prize, Jewel, Gem, Gold Dew, and Mistletoe.

WILSEY FOODS, INC. General office and plant, 633 South Mission Road, Los Angeles, California. Plants are at San Francisco, California; and Salem, Oregon. Established in 1917, it began margarine manufacture in 1964. Consumer and industrial margarines. Principal brands: Western Brand and Table Maid.

MAJOR OILS AND OTHER SUPPLIER FIRMS

Anderson Clayton Foods, Dallas, Texas[1]
Archer Daniels Midland, Decatur, Illinois[1]
Atlas Chemical Industries, Wilmington, Delaware[2]
Central Soya, Fort Wayne, Indiana[1]
Drew Foods & Industrial Chemicals Company, Boonton, New Jersey[1,2,3]
Eastman Chemical Products, Inc., Kingsport, Tennessee[2,3,4]
Glidden-Durkee Division, SCM Corporation, Cleveland, Ohio[1,2]
Hoffman-LaRoche, Inc., Nutley, New Jersey[4,5]
Humko Products, Division of Kraftco Corporation, Memphis, Tennessee[1]
Hunt-Wesson Foods, Inc., Fullerton, California[1,3]
Lever Brothers Company, New York City[1,2]
Pacific Vegetable Oil Products Corporation, San Francisco, California[1]
Pfizer, Inc., New York City[4,5]
Proctor & Gamble Company (The), Cincinnati, Ohio[1]
Redmond and Sons, Inc., Bronx, New York[6]
Riceland Foods—Grains Division, Stuttgart, Arkansas[1]
Riverside Industries, Division of Cook Industries, Inc., Memphis, Tennessee[1]
Swift Edible Oil Company, Chicago[1,3]
B. L. Thomas & Associates, Cincinnati, Ohio[7]
Votator Division of the Chemetron Corporation, Jeffersontown (Louisville), Kentucky[8]

1. Margarine oils and fats; lecithin and other related products. 2. Emulsifiers.
3. Anti-oxidants. 4. Beta carotene. 5. Vitamins. 6. "Reddies" equipment.
7. Margarine technology consultants. 8. Margarine plant equipment.

TABLE I

PRODUCTION OF MARGARINE AND BUTTER, 1886-1969*

Year	Margarine Mil. lb.	Butter[1] Mil. lb.	Year	Margarine Mil. lb.	Butter[1] Mil. lb.
1886	6[2]	1,086	1921	215	1,748
1887	31	1,126	1922	185	1,870
1888	37	1,166	1923	228	1,993
1889	33	1,206	1924	232	2,066
1890	35	1,234	1925	234	2,082
1891	48	1,263	1926	243	2,132
1892	56	1,291	1927	277	2,188
1893	76	1,320	1928	317	2,120
1894	63	1,349	1929	356	2,184
1895	51	1,377	1930	326	2,149
1896	46	1,406	1931	230	2,239
1897	51	1,435	1932	203	2,307
1898	71	1,463	1933	245	2,375
1899	107[3]	1,492	1934	264	2,286
1900	105[3]	1,506	1935	382	2,211
1901	126[3]	1,521	1936	393	2,168
1902	73[3]	1,536	1937	397	2,135
1903	50[3]	1,550	1938	385	2,252
1904	52[3]	1,565	1939	301	2,210
1905	55[3]	1,576	1940	320	2,240
1906	71[3]	1,588	1941	368	2,268
1907	82[3]	1,599	1942	426	2,130
1908	92[3]	1,610	1943	614	2,015
1909	116	1,622	1944	588	1,818
1910	147	1,706	1945	614	1,699
1911	105	1,762	1946	573	1,502
1912	142	1,592	1947	746	1,640
1913	152	1,608	1948	908	1,504
1914	141	1,685	1949	862	1,688
1915	142	1,751	1950	937	1,648
1916	188	1,793	1951	1,041	1,443
1917	287	1,644	1952	1,286	1,402
1918	351	1,503	1953	1,292	1,607
1919	369	1,647	1954	1,364	1,628
1920	369	1,574	1955	1,334	1,545

TABLE I (Continued)
PRODUCTION OF MARGARINE AND BUTTER, 1886-1969*

Year	Margarine Mil. lb.	Butter[1] Mil. lb.	Year	Margarine Mil. lb.	Butter[1] Mil. lb.
1956	1,370	1,553	1963	1,794	1,453
1957	1,463	1,533	1964	1,857	1,468
1958	1,573	1,486	1965	1,904	1,342
1959	1,611	1,411	1966	2,110	1,125
1960	1,695	1,435	1967	2,114	1,246
1961	1,724	1,536	1968	2,141	1,190
1962	1,726	1,579	1969	2,182	1,120

* Figures are rounded by millions. Source: 1886-1908, reports of the U.S. Commissioner of Internal Revenue; 1909-67, reports of the U.S. Department of Agriculture. Colored and uncolored (white) margarine are included. These two categories are separately reported in the reports of the U.S. Commissioner of Internal Revenue for the period 1898-1950 and are given, with other information, for the period 1918-34 in Anne Dewees, *Oleomargarine* (Washington, U.S. Department of Agriculture, 1936), and for the period 1903-1950 in Martha Howard, "The Margarine Industry in the United States" (Ms., Columbia University, 1951). These latter three sources report by fiscal years.

1. Creamery and farm butter combined.

2. Production for November-December 1886, only. For pre-1887 production estimate, see Chapter VII.

3. Fiscal year (July-June).

TABLE II
AVERAGE RETAIL PRICES OF MARGARINE AND BUTTER, 1947-69*
(Cents Per Pound)

Year	Margarine	Butter	Year	Margarine	Butter
1947	40.8	80.5	1959	28.0	75.3
1948	41.4	86.7	1960	26.9	74.9
1949	30.8	72.5	1961	28.6	76.3
1950	31.8	72.9	1962	28.4	75.2
1951	36.0	81.9	1963	27.5	75.0
1952	31.2	85.5	1964	26.0	74.4
1953	29.4	79.0	1965	27.9	75.5
1954	29.9	72.4	1966	28.7	82.2
1955	28.9	70.9	1967	28.4	83.7
1956	28.9	72.1	1968	27.9	83.6
1957	29.9	74.3	1969	27.8	84.6
1958	29.4	74.2			

* Source: U.S. Department of Labor

TABLE III

CIVILIAN PER CAPITA DISAPPEARANCE, MARGARINE AND BUTTER, 1887-1969* (Pounds)

Year	Margarine Actual Weight	Margarine Fat Content	Butter Actual Weight	Year	Margarine Actual Weight	Margarine Fat Content	Butter Actual Weight
1887	.4	.3	19.0	1910	1.6	1.3	18.3
1888	.5	.4	19.3	1911	1.1	.9	18.6
1889	.6	.5	19.4	1912	1.5	1.2	16.6
1890	.5	.4	19.1	1913	1.5	1.3	16.5
1891	.7	.6	19.5	1914	1.4	1.2	17.0
1892	.7	.6	19.6	1915	1.4	1.2	17.2
1893	1.0	.8	19.8	1916	1.8	1.5	17.3
1894	1.0	.8	19.8	1917	2.7	2.3	15.7
1895	.7	.6	19.9	1918	3.3	2.8	14.1
1896	.6	.5	19.7	1919	3.4	2.9	15.2
1897	.6	.5	19.6	1920	3.4	2.9	14.9
1898	.7	.6	19.7	1921	2.0	1.7	16.3
1899	1.1	.9	19.8	1922	1.7	1.4	17.1
1900	1.4	1.1	19.6	1923	2.0	1.7	17.8
1901	1.3	1.0	19.3	1924	2.0	1.7	17.8
1902	1.5	1.2	19.2	1925	2.0	1.7	18.1
1903	.8	.6	19.1	1926	2.0	1.8	18.3
1904	.5	.4	18.8	1927	2.3	2.0	18.3
1905	.5	.4	18.6	1928	2.6	2.3	17.6
1906	.5	.4	18.2	1929	2.9	2.5	17.6
1907	.8	.6	18.2	1930	2.6	2.2	17.6
1908	.9	.7	18.0	1931	1.9	1.5	18.3
1909	1.2	1.1	17.8	1932	1.6	1.3	18.5

(TABLE III (Continued))

CIVILIAN PER CAPITA DISAPPEARANCE, MARGARINE AND BUTTER, 1887-1969* (Pounds)

Year	Margarine Actual Weight	Margarine Fat Content	Butter Actual Weight	Year	Margarine Actual Weight	Margarine Fat Content	Butter Actual Weight
1933	1.9	1.6	18.2	1952	7.9	6.5	8.6
1934	2.1	1.7	18.6	1953	8.1	6.5	8.5
1935	3.0	2.4	17.6	1954	8.5	6.9	8.9
1936	3.1	2.5	16.8	1955	8.2	6.6	9.0
1937	3.1	2.5	16.8	1956	8.2	6.6	8.7
1938	3.0	2.4	16.6	1957	8.6	6.9	8.3
1939	2.3	1.9	17.4	1958	9.0	7.3	8.3
1940	2.4	1.9	17.0	1959	9.2	7.4	7.9
1941	2.8	2.2	16.1	1960	9.4	7.6	7.5
1942	2.8	2.3	15.9	1961	9.4	7.6	7.4
1943	3.9	3.2	11.8	1962	9.3	7.5	7.3
1944	3.9	3.4	11.9	1963	9.6	7.7	6.9
1945	4.1	3.2	10.9	1964	9.7	7.8	6.9
1946	3.9	4.1	10.5	1965	9.9	8.0	6.5
1947	5.0	5.0	11.2	1966	10.5	8.5	5.7
1948	6.1	4.7	10.0	1967	10.5	8.4	5.5
1949	5.8	4.6	10.5	1968	10.5	8.4	5.9
1950	6.1	5.0	10.7	1969	10.8	8.6	5.8
1951	6.6	5.4	9.7				

* From 1887 through 1908 the data are for fiscal years (June 1-May 31). For the remainder they are for calendar years. The fat content figures for 1887-1908 are on the basis of 80% fat. Currently, per capita disappearance figures (sometimes erroneously referred to as "consumption") are reported by the U.S. Department of Agriculture.

Sources for the above data are: 1887-1908, Snodgrass, *op. cit.* pp. 309, 312. 1909-1969, U.S. Department of Agriculture, *U.S. Fats and Oils Situation*, (FOS-252, Washington, April 1970, Table 12.)

151

TABLE IV

FATS AND OILS USED IN MARGARINE, 1947-1969* (Million Pounds)

Year	Vegetable Oils						Animal Fats & Oils			
	Soybean Oil	Corn Oil	Cottonseed Oil	Safflower Oil	Peanut Oil	Other	Lard	Beef Fats	Vegetable Stearine[1]	Total[2]
1947	228	7	323	—	17	21	3	8	—	607
1948	255	1	453	—	11	7	3	6	—	736
1949	257	1	431	—	[a]	—	4	7	—	701
1950	312	1	418	—	7	2	4	9	11	764
1951	473	4	334	—	16	3	4	7	11	851
1952	652	[a]	354	—	3	—	5	13	24	1,046
1953	726	1	275	—	2	6	8	10	12	1,049
1954	665	[a]	397	—	2	7	7	9	17	1,106
1955	746	1	278	—	3	9	13	6	16	1,075
1956	752	[a]	283	—	3	8	31	9	24	1,111
1957	874	[a]	237	—	4	6	25	8	24	1,182
1958	1,070	1	145	—	3	7	16	8	19	1,269
1959	1,094	20	124	—	4	5	36	8	**	1,291
1960	1,105	55	136	—	3	14	56	6	—	1,367
1961	1,062	89	139	6	4	42	72	6	—	1,386
1962	1,058	99	106	22	4	40	70	10	—	1,394
1963	2,049	186	104	12	4	11	84	11	—	1,451
1964	1,139	150	101	10	10	19	64	13	—	1,500
1965	1,112	161	114	46	4	12	100	14	—	1,535
1966	1,294	157	106	42	6	20	82	5	—	1,710
1967	1,249	176	78	42	5	17	125	10	—	1,703
1968	1,240	179	70	42	4	18	153	15	—	1,720
1969	1,334	172	75	43	3	18	86	12	—	1,744

* Source: U.S. Department of Agriculture. Figures are rounded to millions. ** Not reported separately beginning 1959.

[1] Most vegetable stearine used in margarine prior to 1950 was included in the oil.

[2] Includes 2 million pounds of secondary oils other than vegetable stearine in 1952, 3 million in 1953, 1954, 1955 and 1956, and 2 million in 1957 and 1958.

[a] Less than 0.5 million pounds.

Table V
MAJOR RESTRICTIVE MARGARINE LAWS, AS OF JUNE 1970*

Jurisdiction	Per Pound Excise Tax		Annual License Imposed — Fees Charged — Serving Restrictions				Restrictions In State Institutions
	Yellow	White	Retailers	Wholesalers	Public Eating Places	Manufacturers	
Federal [1]							
California	.10[4]	.10[4]			(Serving Restrictions [2]) Restaurants—Boarding Houses—$2.00	$100.00	
Colorado				$ 25.00		$ 25.00	
Idaho	.10[4]	.10[4]					Limited [3]
Kansas							
Massachusetts			$ .50				
Michigan							Limited [3]
Minnesota	.10					$ 5.00	Limited [3]
Montana						$ 20.00 Up	
Nebraska			$3.00	$ 25.00		$100.00	Limited [3]
New York					Restaurants—Boarding Houses—$10.00		
North Carolina	.10[4]	.10[4]					
North Dakota	.10			$ 5.00		$ 10.00	Limited [3]
South Carolina	.10[4]	.10[4]				$ 10.00	
						2 Years	
South Dakota	.10[5]			$ 5.00[6]		$ 5.00	
Tennessee	.10[4]	.10[4]					
Utah	.10[7]	.10[7]					
Vermont			$2.00	$100.00 Up			
Washington							Limited [3]
Wisconsin	.05¼[8]				Serving Restrictions [2]		Limited [3]

(Notes are on next page)

NOTES FOR TABLE V

* This tabulation is based, in part, on interpretations by enforcement officials and does not necessarily reflect the views of anyone else. Not included are certain laws concerning packaging, labeling, notification and federally-donated margarine which may have restrictive effects.

[1] Navy Ration Statute precludes Navy from purchase of yellow or white margarine for table use (10 U.S.C. 6082).

[2] Restaurants may serve yellow margarine only if it is requested by patron.

[3] Does not fully prohibit use under all circumstances: *Idaho*—Margarine prohibited unless no "surplus of butter or other dairy product exists" as determined by the Secretary, U.S. Department of Agriculture, or when ordered by a physician in the course of treatment. *Michigan*—Penal institutions may use margarine. Public schools may use margarine if a physician or dietitian in attendance so recommends. *Minnesota*—Institutions may use margarine on order of the superintendent if directed by a physician for a health reason of a specific inmate or patient. *Nebraska*—Use permitted in certain institutions. *North Dakota*—Institutions allowed to serve margarine if donated, but may not purchase it. *Washington*—Use of margarine prohibited in state institutions except that such institutions may use margarine when supplied for distribution by U.S. Government. *Wisconsin*—Institutions may use margarine on order of the superintendent if directed by a physician for a health reason of a specfic inmate or patient.

[4] Only applies to margarine made from certain fats or oils.

[5] Tax is scheduled to terminate June 30, 1971.

[6] License applies to "distributor," who may be either manufacturing margarine or importing margarine into state for sale to retailers.

[7] Sales to State of Utah and its agencies, and all sales of 25 pounds or more to charitable institutions are exempt from the tax.

[8] Tax terminates, by statute, June 30, 1972.

INDEX